Welcome to Enlighten!

Here at Enlighten our mission is simple. We assist others in transformative healing by sharing the amazing benefits of essential oils. As certified facilitators and students of a variety of energy modalities, our founders offer unique perspectives on combining clinical techniques with powerful all-natural tools. This bestselling book was the very first published on the subject and has been well loved and referenced often.

But it doesn't stop here.

Visit our Website.
We'll help you Discover Oils in New Exciting Ways!

Stop by **www.enlightenhealing.com** where you'll find additional tools and resources.

- Ongoing research and new training on oils and their benefits for emotional healing
- Practical suggestions for using oils day-to-day
- Guidelines to help facilitate emotional breakthroughs
- Access to live events, pre-recorded webinars and audio training
- Resources for continued learning

....

Sharing is Caring — Bulk Discounts Available

Interested in sharing Emotions & Essential Oils *with your clients, family members and teams? We offer bulk order discounts starting at just 10 copies! Visit the website or contact us (customerservice@enlightenhealing.com) for the best bulk pricing available.*

....

.

EMOTIONS & ESSENTIAL OILS

A Modern Resource for Healing

Emotional Reference Guide

Fifth Edition Updated Fall 2016

EMOTIONS & ESSENTIAL OILS
A Modern Resource for Healing
Emotional Reference Guide
Fifth Edition

Published by:

Enlighten Alternative Healing, LLC
PO Box 1444, American Fork, UT 84003
www.enlightenhealing.com

NOTICE TO READERS:

"The medical school of the future will not particularly interest itself in the ultimate results and products of disease, nor will it pay so much attention to actual physical lesions, or administer drugs and chemicals merely for the sake of palliating our symptoms, but knowing the true cause of sickness and aware that the obvious physical results are merely secondary, it will concentrate its efforts upon bringing about that harmony between body, mind and soul which results in the relief and cure of disease"

"Amongst the types of remedies that will be used will be those obtained from the most beautiful plants and herbs to be found in the pharmacy of Nature, such as have been divinely enriched with healing powers for the mind and body of man"

— *Dr. Edward Bach, from* Heal Thyself: An Explanation of the Real Cause and Cure of Disease

TABLE OF CONTENTS

Section I: Healing with Essential Oils

Section II: Oil Descriptions

SINGLE OILS

OIL BLENDS

Section III: Appendices

SECTION I

HEALING WITH ESSENTIAL OILS

KALLIE'S STORY

The following true story, written by Kallie's mother, perfectly embodies the steps involved in emotional healing—from the time of trauma, through the healing crisis, and on to wholeness. It beautifully illustrates how the use of essential oils facilitates physical, emotional, and spiritual healing. We sincerely thank Kallie and her family for allowing their story to be included in this book.

When my daughter Kallie was two years old, she accidentally pulled a slow cooker full of boiling meat down onto herself, severely burning her face and torso. Second- and third-degree burns covered a third of her body. For a month, Kallie recuperated in a special burn unit where she received heavy narcotics along with other medications to help numb the intense pain that accompanies such severe burns. Two surgeries were necessary to place skin grafts on her face, neck, and shoulders. When Kallie finally came home, she had to wear a plastic mask on her face and a tight-fitting body suit for six months to keep the skin grafts from warping.

As her mother, it was horrifying to see my child suffer so much pain; I felt helpless. But Kallie was a very strong girl who tried her best to adapt to the excruciating medical procedures, such as having the dead skin scrubbed from the burned area or working through physical therapy. During the many times when the pain and trauma were too much for little Kallie, she would mentally leave us. I could see it in her hollow eyes. The first time I saw this was when the initial burn happened. In those few seconds right after the hot liquid touched her precious skin, she wasn't there. Due to the combination of heavy narcotics and unbearable procedures, she was physically and emotionally numb or just plain absent during most of the month that she was hospitalized. After we got home, it took a while to get back to regular life.

3

Kallie was just so fragile and delicate. I tried my absolute best to physically and emotionally recover her and our family from this event, but it was quite a challenge.

The months and years went by, and I started to notice that Kallie was extremely numb to pain. She was a very active, adventurous girl and had quite a few falls and injuries just like any other child, but she rarely acknowledged that it hurt her. Sometimes it was disturbing. I remember one visit to the doctor for her regular vaccines. Kallie lay down on the table, and the two nurses poked both her legs two times each. I watched her face and there was absolutely no physical or emotional reaction whatsoever. She was unfeeling. She often got nasty gashes or scrapes, and I wouldn't even know about them until later when I gave her a bath or changed her clothes. I would ask where she got hurt and a lot of times she didn't even remember. She was also very self-conscious of the physical changes the burn had caused. When Kallie began school, she tried to hide her scars by covering them with her hair or coat or by walking with her face pointed toward the wall and away from onlookers.

I never pushed her to talk about it or do anything that was uncomfortable for her, but I gently tried to give her opportunities to share her thoughts and feelings. When Kallie was about five and a half, she started to forget what happened. She knew that something big occurred a long time ago, but she couldn't remember the details. Sometimes there was a trigger that sparked her memory, like the word "burn," or a fire, or even a bath. Then with fear and confusion in her eyes, she would start asking, "What happened to me, Mom?" Around this time, I was introduced to essential oils. As my mother and I learned about the oils and their benefits, we thought of Kallie. Helichrysum and Vetiver seemed like the perfect fit, and we began treatment. I was so excited in the beginning, mostly thinking of the potential physical healing and largely unaware of the emotional benefits.

Kallie was full of faith. She immediately said, "I know it's gonna make my burn melt away, Mom!" I had no idea what was coming.

After only a few days of using the oils, Kallie started to act differently. The first thing I noticed was that she started to complain of physical pain for which we could find no reasonable explanation. Every time she got the smallest cut or bruise, she had major anxiety about it—very opposite from her recent tough, numb-to-pain reactions. She cried for hours about tiny cuts or slivers and would say through tears, "Is it ever gonna go away?" Kallie spent a large portion of the day worrying about the smallest things. It was almost impossible to convince her to take a bath. She became extremely picky about the clothes she wore. If clothing touched her "wrong" or was at all tight, she wouldn't wear it. Any mention of her being burned or even the word "burn" caused extreme fear. Anxiety attacks surfaced. Sometimes she randomly sat on my lap and just cried. I would cry too.

I finally realized Kallie was going through a healing crisis brought on by the oils. It made perfect sense. Every odd thing that she was doing directly correlated to the burn or to her experience in the hospital. With the help of essential oils, her body was expelling or ejecting all of the pain and hidden emotions that were buried for so long.

We guessed that the healing would probably last for the same amount of time she had stayed in the hospital. This was exactly right. It lasted a month. I tried my best to validate what she was feeling and to help her as much as I could during this time. I learned that if I missed a day of putting on her oils, it was a bad day for her and the rest of the household! So I kept up with it, and the results were phenomenal.

After this difficult month, I began to notice that words which had previously triggered a negative reaction from Kallie did not seem to bother her. She had a totally new and positive perspective.

I could see plain as day that she was no longer coming from a place of fear. Instead of being self-conscious or shy, she was secure, strong, and confident—a totally different Kallie.

As her mom, I can see without a doubt that these essential oils gave her such a beautiful new outlook on herself and her past traumatic experience. On the morning of Kallie's seventh birthday, I told her about the day she was born, and she said, "I don't remember that, Mom, but I do remember when I was burned." I carefully asked, "What do you feel when you remember it?" She replied in her bubbly, secure voice, "Let me spell it for you mom: OK!" Words cannot express how very grateful I am that my little Kallie could heal emotionally.

HEALING EMOTIONS
WITH ESSENTIAL OILS

As illustrated in Kallie's story, essential oils play a powerful role in emotional healing. They lead us by the hand as we courageously face our emotional issues. Kallie is not the only one with repressed emotional trauma. We all hold unresolved feelings of pain and hurt which need to be brought to the surface for transformation and healing.

Essential Oils: Five Stages of Healing

Essential oils support healing in five stages. They strengthen us during each stage and prepare us for the next level of healing. For example, as we regain our physical health, we are invited to enter the emotional realm.

In this book we briefly explore stage one and mainly focus on defining stage two: the emotional stage. While we briefly touch on concepts from stages three through five in the oil descriptions, they are largely topics for another book.

The Five Stages are:

1. Essential oils assist in healing the physical body.

2. Essential oils assist in healing the heart.

3. Essential oils assist in releasing limiting beliefs.

4. Essential oils increase spiritual awareness and connection.

5. Essential oils inspire the fulfillment of our life's purpose.

Stage One: Healing the Physical Body

Essential oils are powerful physical healers. Some essential oils are considered to be 40 to 60 times more potent than herbs (Schnaubelt, 2011). Essential oils assist the body in fighting unfriendly microorganisms; purifying organs, glands, and body systems; balancing body functions; and raising the body's vibration (Stewart, 2003).

Stage Two: Healing the Heart

As the oils secure our physical health, they provide us with the energy needed to penetrate the heart and enter the emotional realm. Essential oils raise the vibration of the physical body (Stewart, 2003). As the body lives in higher vibrations, lower energies (such as suppressed emotions) become unbearable. The body wants to release these feelings. Stagnant anger, sadness, grief, judgment, and low self-worth cannot exist in the environment of balance and peace which essential oils help to create.

Emotional healing occurs as old feelings surface and release (Moreton, 1992). Sometimes this experience is confused with regression. People may perceive they are going backwards or that the essential oils are not working. We are so used to symptomatic healing that we have been conditioned to view healing as the immediate cessation of all physical and emotional pain. In reality, the oils are working. They are working to permanently heal emotional issues by supporting individuals through their healing.

Principles of Healing: Release and Receive

It is important to understand that healing is a process. The process can be separated into two main principles: release and receive.

We must release trapped negative emotions before we can receive positive feelings. The old must go to make space for the new. We often want to skip this step, but it is a necessary one. We must be willing to experience the cleansing if we truly desire healing. Resisting the cleansing process makes healing more painful. We must surrender to the experience so that we may continue on the path of healing. The more we let go and trust, the more enjoyable this healing process can be.

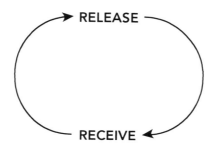

Essential Oils Don't Do Our Emotional Work for Us

Essential oils assist individuals in taking an honest look within. They foster the right environment for healing, but they will not do the work for us. In gardening, it is a common mistake to pull the weeds while leaving the roots. This is particularly true for hard and rocky soils. To ensure we uproot the whole plant, we can add water to the soil, which allows the entire weed to be removed. Similarly, essential oils prepare our emotional soil so that weeds may be removed with greater ease. However, they do not do the weeding for us. If we neglect to do the work of pulling our weeds, we have simply watered the problem. On the other hand, when we combine essential oils with emotional work, we reap the fruit of our labor.

Tools for Emotional Work

You may be wondering, "How do I begin my emotional work?" We propose that individuals begin their emotional work with a few introductory practices. We suggest meditation, journaling, and personal inventory to facilitate the healing process. We invite everyone to embark on their own healing path and believe this book will greatly assist you and your family.

A WORD ON QUALITY

Three Categories of Essential Oils:

1. Aromatic Essential Oils

2. Therapeutic-Grade Essential Oils

3. Independently Tested Therapeutic-Grade Essential Oils

The first category applies to many oils marketed for their scent and aromatic properties. These essential oils are widely available in health food stores. It is important to know that these essential oils are often not therapeutic grade and should not be used topically or internally, as they are not for medicinal use. These oils are usually synthetic and therefore harmful to the body. They have no therapeutic value.

The second category of essential oils is therapeutic-grade oils. Many companies fall into this category. The intent of these companies is to provide quality essential oils that can be used for healing. These oils are for topical and aromatic use. Great care should be taken when purchasing these oils, as they are often diluted with synthetic chemicals or other additives.

The third category of essential oils is independently tested therapeutic-grade oils. These oils are tested at independent laboratories with tests such as gas chromatography and mass spectrometry to verify their purity and composition. Oils that meet rigorous testing and are considered safe by the Food and Drug Administration may be considered for topical use. Never use any essential oil internally that is not "generally recognized as safe (GRAS)" for dietary consumption by the FDA. Also consult with a healthcare professional. Only the highest-quality essential oils should be used for physical, emotional, and spiritual healing.

© Enlighten

HOW TO USE ESSENTIAL OILS

Please reference all safety information when using essential oils for aromatic, topical, or internal use. (See "A Word on Quality" in this section.)

Aromatic

To use an essential oil aromatically, simply smell the oil directly from the bottle. You may also place a few drops into a diffuser which disperses the oil into the air. Another option is to place a few drops of the essential oil into the palms of the hands, rub together vigorously, and inhale deeply.

Topical

To use an essential oil topically, place a few drops in the palm of the hand and apply to selected area(s). Essential oils are potent, so a small amount should be sufficient. It is recommended that you dilute the oil with a carrier such as fractionated coconut oil. If applying more than one oil to the same place on your body, be sure to layer the oils rather than mixing them together first and applying them as a mixture. Layering means to apply the oils one at a time. Allow a few minutes for each oil to absorb into the skin before adding the next one.

Caution: Use wisdom and consider all safety information from a competent reference book regarding essential oil use. There are some oils that should never be taken internally. Others should not be applied "neat," or directly on the skin, without first being diluted with a carrier oil. Also ensure the oils you are using are of the highest standards of quality. (See "A Word on Quality" in this section.) Use caution when using essential oils for children and babies. Some oils may not be safe for children or for use during pregnancy. Please read the instructions on the bottle, or check with the manufacturer to determine the safe uses of the oils. Essential oils can be much more potent than herbs, so a little goes a long way. Babies and children have highly sensitive skin and require less oil. If you are pregnant or nursing, consult a licensed healthcare professional before using essential oils.

HOW TO USE THIS BOOK

Oil Descriptions

The main body of this book is divided into individual descriptions of the oils. The single oils are listed first and oil blends are next. Read the individual or blend descriptions to determine which essential oil would be best suited for your emotional needs. You may then reference the usage guide in Appendix D.

Usage Guide

In the Essential Oil Emotional Usage Guide (Appendix D), you may search for specific emotional states and find the recommended oil(s) which supports those states.

Companion to Modern Essentials

This book may also be used as a companion to *Modern Essentials*, which serves as a reference guide to your physical health and application of essential oils. After finding the recommended oils for your physical condition, cross-reference those oils with the emotional descriptions found in this book. For the most powerful results, choose the oil(s) that matches your emotional state as well as your physical condition.

Citations

Moreton, V. S. (1992). *A New Day in Healing!* (pp. 16-17). San Diego, CA: Kalos Publishing.

Schnaubelt, K. (2011). *The Healing Intelligence of Essential Oils.* (pp. 13-16). Rochester, VT: Healing Arts Press.

Stewart, D. (2003). *Healing Oils of the Bible.* (pp. 31-34). Marble Hill, MO: Care Publications.

(2015). *Modern Essentials.* (7th ed.). Spanish Fork, UT: Aroma Tools. DOI: www.AromaTools.com

SECTION II

OIL DESCRIPTIONS

SINGLE OILS

ARBORVITAE
The Oil of Divine Grace

Arborvitae assists individuals who believe or act like all progress must be made through struggle and solitary effort. Instead of trusting in the Divine, these individuals unconsciously block Divine aid, choosing instead to live by their own efforts. Arborvitae addresses the need to control one's outcomes in life. It invites individuals to live with peace and joy by trusting in the abundant flow of Divine grace.

Arborvitae is also a grounding oil that teaches Divinity is all around. God's grace can be felt and experienced here on earth; it is not distant or separate. God can help find balance in life and teach what to hold close and what to release.

Arborvitae's Latin name means "to sacrifice." This oil invites individuals to sacrifice their personal will and ambitions for a far more fulfilling way of living. By surrendering to God, the mind relaxes and the soul experiences harmony and peace. Arborvitae teaches that true strength can come through emptiness or a willingness to receive God's strength. It asks individuals to relax, take a deep breath, and trust in the flow of life. Arborvitae assists the soul to live effortlessly by Divine grace.

Negative Emotions: Willful, struggle, excessive effort, distrust, rigid, fearful, need to control

Positive Properties: Peaceful, surrender, grounded, allowing, relaxed, grace-filled, effortless living, trust in Divine grace

19

BASIL
The Oil of Renewal

The symptoms of adrenal exhaustion help identify the main moods that are improved with Basil, primarily fatigue, low energy, being overwhelmed, and the inability to cope with life's stressors. The smell of Basil oil brings strength to the heart and relaxation to the mind. This oil is also excellent for states of nervousness, anxiousness, and despair.

Basil oil supports those who are under a great deal of mental strain. It brings rejuvenation of vital forces after long periods of burnout and exhaustion. Basil oil may strengthen the adrenals and restore the body to its natural rhythms of sleep, activity, and rest.

Basil oil is also helpful for recovery from negative habits. It gives hope and optimism to the tired soul. Basil may assist an individual in giving up false stimulants or helping with substance abuse. By increasing one's natural energy, it supports individuals to achieve greater balance and health. In short, Basil is indicated for those who are weary in mind and body and for those in need of strength and renewal.

Negative Emotions: Anxious, weary, overwhelmed, tired, drained, exhausted, negative habits

Positive Properties: Energized, renewed, rejuvenated, rested, strengthened

BERGAMOT
The Oil of Self-Acceptance

Bergamot relieves feelings of despair, self-judgment, and low self-esteem. It supports the individual in need of self-acceptance and self-love. Bergamot invites individuals to see life with more optimism.

Bergamot has a cleansing effect on stagnant feelings and limiting belief systems. Because of individuals' core beliefs of being "bad," "unlovable," and "not good enough," they seek to hide behind a façade of cheerfulness. They may fear revealing their true thoughts and feelings. Bergamot's powerful cleansing properties generate movement in the energy system, which in turn brings hope.

In this way, Bergamot is wonderful for those who feel down and hopeless. It awakens the soul to hope and offers courage to share the inner self. Reigniting optimism and confidence in the Self, it imparts true self-acceptance. Bergamot teaches individuals to let go of self-judgment by learning to love themselves unconditionally.

Negative Emotions: Despair, low self-esteem, self-judgment, unlovable, hopeless

Positive Properties: Self-acceptance, optimism, confidence, hopeful, lovable, good enough

© Enlighten

BIRCH
The Oil of Support

Birch offers support to the unsupported. When a person is feeling attacked or unsupported by family or friends, Birch offers courage to move forward alone. Learning to be flexible is important, but so is gaining a strong backbone. Birch offers support to the weak-willed to stand tall and firm in what they believe.

Birch helps individuals to feel their roots, specifically their connection to family and ancestors. Birch is a tree that stands tall and firm and assists others in doing the same. It assists in overcoming negative generational patterns, especially in situations where one is at risk of being rejected if they choose a different way. It lends its spirit of endurance to help individuals face trials of adversity, so they may weather storms with the strength and conviction of a tree.

Birch teaches there is more to life than pain, and that with the right support and the right grounding, one can be held up and sustained by Divine grace.

Negative Emotions: Unsupported, alienated, fear, weak-willed, overly flexible

Positive Properties: Supported, firm, resolute, strong, grounded, connected

BLACK PEPPER
The Oil of Unmasking

Black Pepper reveals the masks and façades used to hide aspects of the Self. Since childhood, most individuals have been taught that some feelings and behaviors are "good" while others are not. So instead of seeking to understand seemingly inappropriate feelings and behaviors, they usually judge, condemn, and repress them. Individuals learn early on that to be loved and accepted, they must hide undesirable aspects of themselves behind a mask or façade.

Black Pepper invites individuals to get real by digging deep within the less understood parts of the Self. Whether one's true motives and feelings are acknowledged or not, they continue to exist. The more these feelings are pushed down, buried, and repressed, the more they seek to make themselves known. If they are not honestly dealt with and acknowledged, they will often be expressed through erratic, compulsive, or obsessive behaviors.

Black Pepper also reignites the soul fire, fueling motivation and high energy and hastening the healing process. It gives an individual strength to overcome the challenges and issues they carry inside and invites them to live in integrity with the Self.

Negative Emotions: Emotional dishonesty, repressed emotions, feeling trapped, prideful, superficial, judgmental

Positive Properties: Emotional honesty, authentic, courageous, motivated, self-aware, personal integrity

23

CARDAMOM
The Oil of Objectivity

Cardamom helps individuals to regain objectivity, mental sobriety, and self-control. It assists individuals who frequently feel frustrated or angry with other people. Cardamom is especially helpful for times when one's anger goes to their head, causing them to become hotheaded. In such situations, the individual becomes inebriated with anger, losing control and rational function. Cardamom helps to bring balance, mental clarity, and objectivity during moments of extreme anger and frustration.

Cardamom is especially beneficial for individuals with a long history of anger or aggression, which often becomes directed outward. It is helpful for those who hyper-focus on their problems, especially their frustrations. Cardamom assists individuals to break down or "digest" these intense emotions of frustration and anger by redirecting energy to the solar plexus, the center of responsibility. In this way, Cardamom helps individuals let go of emotional distortions which cause them to objectify other people and see them as inconveniences.

Cardamom demands that individuals stop blaming others. It asks them to take personal ownership and responsibility for their feelings. As they do, they will feel more at peace, calm, and in control of themselves.

Negative Emotions: Inebriated by anger, easily frustrated, objectifying others, blaming, unable to think clearly

Positive Properties: Objectivity, self-control, respectful, tolerant, patient, mental sobriety

CASSIA
The Oil of Self-Assurance

Cassia brings gladness and courage to the heart and soul. It is a wonderful remedy for the shy and timid. It helps those who hold back and try to hide. When a person avoids being the center of attention, Cassia can restore their confidence.

Similar to Cinnamon, Cassia dispels fear and replaces it with self-assurance. It challenges an individual to try, even when they are afraid of making mistakes. Cassia aids those who feel foolish by helping them see their own brilliance. It supports the soul in seeing its own value and potential. Cassia assists the individual in discovering their innate gifts and talents. It invites one to let their light shine and live from their authentic Self.

Negative Emotions: Embarrassed, hiding, fear, humiliated, insecure, judged, shy, worthless

Positive Properties: Courageous, self-assured, unashamed, confidence, valuable, authentic

CEDARWOOD
The Oil of Community

Cedarwood brings people together to experience the strength and value of community. Those in need of Cedarwood struggle to form bonds within social groups. This can often be due to an overdeveloped sense of individuality. Rather than allowing oneself to be supported by family, friends, or a community, they live by excessive self-reliance. On the other hand, the individual's difficulty forming social roots may also stem from feeling disconnected and separate from the human family. Cedarwood inspires the feeling of belonging and assists the heart in opening to receive the love and support of other people. It invites the strong-willed individual to couple the strength of individuality with the supportive power of community.

Cedarwood supports individuals in seeing that they are not alone; life is a shared experience. Cedarwood also assists in opening the awareness of individuals to the support system that is already available to them, such as friends or family that have been overlooked. It invites individuals to both give and receive, so they may experience the strength of groups and the joy of relationships.

Negative Emotions: Inability to form bonds or social roots, loneliness, feeling disconnected or separate from the human family, antisocial

Positive Properties: Connected, belonging, supported, social bonds, neighborly, joy in relationships

CILANTRO
The Oil of Releasing Control

Cilantro facilitates a detoxification of negative emotions and debris. It is helpful in lightening one's load through the release of issues buried in the body, heart, and soul. Similar to Coriander oil, which is distilled from the seeds of the same plant, Cilantro assists individuals in shedding what is not in harmony with their True Self.

Those in need of Cilantro may attempt to obsessively control other people or manage their environment. Inwardly, these individuals may experience a great deal of worry and mental strain. The person may become constricted, clinging to or obsessing over material possessions. The individual may even hold onto the very patterns, emotions, issues, and possessions which may impair or betray their True Self.

Cilantro facilitates emotional cleansing, and especially encourages the release of worry and control as it assists individuals in centering in their True Self. Cilantro liberates the soul from heavy burdens, enabling the individual to live light and free.

Negative Emotions: Controlling, toxic, constricted, obsessive, clingy, emotionally trapped

Positive Properties: Cleansing, liberated, unattached, ease, lightened

CINNAMON
The Oil of Sexual Harmony

Cinnamon supports the reproductive system and helps heal sexual issues. It assists individuals in accepting their body and embracing their physical attractiveness. Cinnamon dispels fear of rejection and nurtures healthy sexuality. It rekindles sexual energies when there has been repression, trauma, or abuse. It can also bring clarity to souls who struggle with their sexual identity.

Cinnamon also assists individuals in relationships where insecurities are shown by jealousy or control. It encourages the soul to let go of control and allow others to be free. Cinnamon can nurture strong relationships based on mutual love and respect.

Where there are other insecurities covered by pretense, façade, and pride, Cinnamon invites individuals to be honest and vulnerable, thereby allowing true intimacy to emerge.

Negative Emotions: Body rejection, fear, controlling, jealousy, sexual abuse, sexual repression or overactive sexuality

Positive Properties: Body-acceptance, attractive, accepted, healthy sexuality, harmonious, intimacy

CLARY SAGE
The Oil of Clarity & Vision

Clary Sage assists individuals in changing their perceptions. It gives courage to "see" the truth. One of the finest oils for the brow chakra, Clary Sage dispels darkness and illusion, helping a person to see their limiting belief systems. Clary Sage encourages individuals to remain open to new ideas and new perspectives. It can assist during a healing crisis when a drastic change of perspective is required. Clary Sage opens the soul to new possibilities and experiences.

Clary Sage assists in opening creative channels and clearing creative blocks. It eliminates distractions from the mind and assists individuals in finding a state of emptiness where creative forces may be realized. Opening individuals to the dream world, Clary Sage increases one's ability to visualize and imagine new possibilities.

Clary Sage teaches the spirit how to use its divinely given gifts and is especially helpful in clarifying spiritual vision. It assists in developing the gift of discernment. Clary Sage invites individuals to expand their vision and accept the reality of the spiritual world.

Negative Emotions: Confusion, darkness, discouragement, disconnection from spiritual realms, hopeless, blocked creativity

Positive Properties: Clarity, intuitive, open-minded, imaginative, spiritually discerning

CLOVE
The Oil of Boundaries

Clove supports individuals in letting go of victim mentality. Victims feel overly influenced by other people and outside circumstances. They perceive themselves as powerless to change their life situations. Clove helps individuals to stand up for themselves, be proactive, and feel capable of making their own decisions, regardless of others' opinions or responses.

Clove assists individuals in letting go of patterns of self-betrayal and codependency by reconnecting them with their personal integrity. It builds up appropriate boundaries and defenses.

Clove gives the pushover the courage to say "no." It reignites the inner soul fire and can assist anytime there has been damage to the Self related to childhood pain, trauma, or abuse. Clove is especially helpful for breaking free of patterns of abuse by restoring the victim's sense of Self and helping them regain the strength to stand up for their needs. Clove insists that individuals live true to themselves and the Divine by establishing clear boundaries.

Negative Emotions: Victim, defeated, dominated, enslaved, fear of rejection, intimidated, controlled by others, codependent

Positive Properties: Empowered, clear boundaries, protected, courageous, independent, capable, proactive, personal integrity

CORIANDER
The Oil of Integrity

Coriander is the oil of integrity, specifically integrity with one's self. The person in need of Coriander oil may be trapped in a cycle of serving others while neglecting their own needs. They may also have a strong desire to do what is right or correct. Often the mind's perspective of the "right" way is too limited and seen from only one perspective. Coriander reminds individuals that there is more than one way to do something, and that fitting in often requires betraying the True Self.

Coriander moves the individual from doing things for the acceptance of others to honoring and living from the True Self. There are as many ways of being as there are people in the world. Each soul must learn its own way of living and being. Coriander gives courage to step out of the box and risk being who one really is.

Coriander teaches that each individual is a gift to the world with something unique, which no one else has to offer. Only they can express their uniqueness. Integrity with one's self means living in connection with what one's spirit urges and directs. Coriander helps individuals live from the True Self.

Negative Emotions: Controlled by others, self-betrayal, drudgery, conforming

Positive Properties: True to self, inner guidance, integrity, unique

CYPRESS
The Oil of Motion & Flow

This powerful oil creates energetic flow and emotional catharsis. Stagnant energies are brought into motion through the fluid energy of this oil. Cypress works in the heart and mind, creating flexibility.

Cypress teaches the soul how to let go of the past by moving with the flow of life. This oil is especially indicated for individuals who are mentally or emotionally stuck, stiff, rigid, tense, over- striving, or have perfectionistic tendencies. This hard-driving stems from fear and the need to control. The individual tries to force things in life rather than allowing them to unfold naturally.

Cypress encourages individuals to cast aside their worries and let go of control so they can enjoy the thrill that comes from being alive. It reminds individuals that "damnation" is simply the discontinuation of growth and development, and invites them to step out of the way and allow life to flow freely or without compulsion. Cypress shows how to have perfect trust in the flow of life.

Negative Emotions: Controlling, fear, perfectionism, rigidity, stuck, tense

Positive Properties: Flexible, trust, flowing with life, adaptable, emotional growth

DILL
The Oil of Learning

Dill supports individuals in learning new things, thinking rationally, and integrating different thoughts into coherent ideas.

This oil is especially helpful for those who feel despondent, bored, or disinterested in the learning process. It supports those who have a difficult time engaging, especially in the classroom. Dill is helpful for those individuals who may feel overwhelmed by too many ideas or by too much stimulus in their environment. Dill can assist individuals to digest and integrate all this information. It supports the left and right brain to work together harmoniously. It can also assist individuals in overcoming mental sluggishness by encouraging awake, alert involvement.

Dill encourages individuals to embrace the many facets of life by engaging in the learning process. It challenges individuals to become self-motivated learners and to find excitement for discovering new things. It assists individuals in assimilating different thoughts and ideas.

Negative Emotions: Bored, disinterested, disengaged, overstimulated

Positive Properties: Engaged, motivated, integration

© Enlighten

DOUGLAS FIR
The Oil of Generational Wisdom

Douglas and White Fir share many similar qualities. They both address generational issues by inviting individuals to break free from destructive traditions passed down through their families. Like White Fir, Douglas Fir assists individuals to live according to their own conscience and values by letting go of harmful patterns. It teaches that each generation can be a gift of new life, new growth, and new beginnings. Similarly, Douglas Fir can also assist with increasing the bond within one's family. It encourages healthy family dynamics where people and meaningful relationships are valued over blind loyalty to traditions.

Additionally, Douglas Fir teaches individuals to learn from and value others' experiences, especially one's family and ancestors. It encourages respect for one's elders and ancestral heritage. Douglas Fir reminds individuals that valuable wisdom can be obtained by learning from the past, especially from individuals who are older, wiser, and more experienced.

Negative Emotions: Negative generational patterns, burdened by the issues of others

Positive Properties: Generational healing, respect for elders, wisdom, learning from the past

EUCALYPTUS
The Oil of Wellness

The strong medicinal aroma of Eucalyptus demonstrates its powerful effect upon the physical and emotional bodies. Eucalyptus oil supports the soul who is constantly facing illness. They may get well for times and seasons, only to return to a common cold, allergies, or congestion in the sinuses and respiratory system.

Eucalyptus addresses a deep emotional or spiritual issue of the need to be sick. It reveals patterns of thinking that continually create poor health. These beliefs may include thoughts such as "I don't deserve to be well," "I am the sort of person that is always getting sick," or "The only way I can get a break is to get sick." Eucalyptus gives an individual courage to face these issues and beliefs. It encourages them to let go of their attachments to illness.

Eucalyptus encourages individuals to take full responsibility for their own health. It also bestows trust that one's needs and desires can be met, even if they allow themselves to be well. Eucalyptus teaches how to claim wholeness and heal.

Negative Emotions: Attached to illness, clingy, defeated, despair, desire to escape life or responsibilities, imprisoned, powerless to heal, sickly

Positive Properties: Able to heal, well, liberated, responsible, encouraged

FENNEL

The Oil of Responsibility

Fennel supports the individual who has a weakened sense of Self. The individual may feel defeated by life's responsibilities, having little or no desire to improve their situation. Fennel reignites a passion for life. It encourages the soul to take full ownership and responsibility for its choices. Fennel teaches that life is not too much or too big to handle.

Fennel encourages an individual to live in integrity with themselves, despite the judgments of others. When one has been paralyzed by fear and shame, this oil gets them moving again. Fennel reestablishes a strong connection to the body and the Self when there has been weakness or separation.

Fennel also supports an individual in listening to the subtle messages of the body. This is especially important in situations where there has been a loss of connection to the body's natural signals due to emotional eating, severe dieting, eating issues, or drug abuse. Through attunement with the body's actual needs, Fennel curbs cravings for experiences that dull the senses. This oil then supports the individual in hearing the body's signals of hunger, thirst, satiation, tiredness, or exhaustion. Fennel is also supportive in regaining one's appetite for nourishment, food, and life itself.

Negative Emotions: Lack of desire, unwilling to take responsibility for self or life, shame, weak sense of Self, numb to body signals

Positive Properties: Responsible, in tune with body, satiated, maturity

FRANKINCENSE
The Oil of Truth

Frankincense reveals deceptions and false truths. It invites individuals to let go of lower vibrations, lies, deceptions, and negativity. This oil helps create new perspectives based on light and truth. Frankincense recalls to memory spiritual understanding, gifts, wisdom, and knowledge the soul brought into the world. It is a powerful cleanser of spiritual darkness. Frankincense assists in pulling the "scales of darkness" from the eyes, the barriers from the mind, and the walls from the heart. Through connecting the soul with its inner light, this oil reveals the truth.

Frankincense supports in creating a healthy attachment with one's father. It assists in spiritual awakening and helps an individual feel the fatherly love of the Divine. When one has felt abandoned or forgotten, Frankincense reminds them that they are loved and protected. While this oil is incredibly powerful, it is also gentle, like a loving father who nurtures, guides, and protects. Frankincense shields the body and soul from negative influences and assists the soul in its spiritual evolution. Enhancing practices of prayer and meditation, this oil opens spiritual channels that allow an individual to connect to God. Through the light and power of Frankincense, the individual can draw closer to divinity, healthy masculinity, and the grandeur of the True Self.

Negative Emotions: Abandonment, spiritually disconnected, distant from father, unprotected, spiritual darkness

Positive Properties: Enlightened, loved, protected, wisdom, discernment, spiritually open, connection with father

GERANIUM
The Oil of Love & Trust

Geranium restores confidence in the innate goodness of others and in the world. It facilitates trust, especially when an individual has lost trust in others due to difficult life circumstances. It also assists in reestablishing a strong bond to one's mother and father. When there has been a loss of trust in relationships, geranium encourages emotional honesty, love, and forgiveness. It fosters receptivity to human love and connection.

Geranium aids in healing the broken heart. It encourages emotional honesty by facilitating the emergence of grief or pain that has been suppressed. Geranium softens anger and assists in healing emotional wounds. It assists in reopening the heart so that love may flow freely. Indeed, Geranium could be called "the emotional healer."

Geranium is a gentle oil, perfect for babies and children. It nurtures the inner child and supports in re-parenting this aspect of the Self. The individual who has a difficult time accessing their emotions can be supported by Geranium, as it leads away from the logical mind and into the warmth and nurture of the heart. At its root, Geranium heals the heart, instills unconditional love, and fosters trust.

Negative Emotions: Abandonment, loss, distrusting, unforgiving, unloving, disheartened, heavyhearted, grief

Positive Properties: Emotional healing, trusting, forgiving, gentle, loving, tolerant, open

GINGER
The Oil of Empowerment

Ginger holds no reservations. This oil has a purpose and will fulfill it! Ginger powerfully persuades individuals to be fully present and participate in life. It teaches that to be successful in life, one must be wholly committed to it.

Ginger addresses deep patterns of victim mentality, which is evidenced by feelings of powerlessness, believing everything is outside one's control, refusing to take responsibility for life, or blaming life circumstances on other people or outside influences. The victim feels stuck as they decentralize or disown responsibility and blame others for their misfortunes.

Ginger empowers individuals in taking complete responsibility for their life circumstances. It infuses a warrior-like mentality based on personal integrity, centralized responsibility, and individual choice. Here, the individual sees themselves as the creator of their own life. No longer waiting for outside circumstances to change, they choose their own destiny. The empowered individual assumes full responsibility and accountability for the consequences of their actions or inactions.

Negative Emotions: Victim, powerless, unwilling to take responsibility for self or life, defeated, not present, stuck, blaming

Positive Properties: Empowered, capable, purposeful, accountable, responsible

GRAPEFRUIT
The Oil of Honoring the Body

Grapefruit teaches true respect and appreciation for one's physical body. It supports individuals who struggle to honor their body and are caught in patterns of mistreatment. These forms of abuse may include severe dieting, judging one's body weight or type, and abusing the body through negligent behavior or violence. These acts are often motivated by hate and disgust buried within the psyche which gets directed toward the physical body. Though the individual may obsess over how they look, deep down they never feel they look good enough. There is a dissatisfaction that persists.

Grapefruit oil is often misused in overly strict dietary and weight-loss programs. The reason this oil helps curb emotional eating is because it encourages a positive relationship with one's body based on love, tolerance, and acceptance. Grapefruit en- courages integrity by respecting one's physical needs. This oil assists an individual in listening to their true physical needs and impulses. It also assists one in taking responsibility for what they feel. Grapefruit teaches that no amount of food can fill a hole in the heart—only love can do that. As the individual takes ownership of their feelings and gets the help they need in addressing them, they no longer have a need to hide their feelings behind food, body abuse, strict regimens, eating issues, or other forms of obsession.

Negative Emotions: Hate for the body, obsession with food or dieting, eating issues, anxiety over appearance

Positive Properties: Respect for body, meeting physical needs, body-acceptance, nourished, healthy relationship with food

HELICHRYSUM
The Oil for Pain

Helichrysum is an amazing healer of pain. It aids "the walking wounded"—those with a history of difficult life circumstances, trauma, self-destruction, loss, or abuse. These individuals need the powerful spiritual support that Helichrysum offers. It gives strength and endurance to the wounded soul who must keep on living, despite past difficulties. This oil restores confidence in life and in the Self, giving the individual strength to carry on. Helichrysum has a powerful relationship with the light of the sun. It imbues joy, fervor, and hope for living. Helichrysum takes the hurt soul by the hand, guiding them through life's difficulties. If the individual can persevere, this oil can take them into new heights of spiritual consciousness. Helichrysum offers hope that their wounds can be healed.

Following this spiritual healing and transformation, Helichrysum can teach an individual to have gratitude for their trials. It helps one to see that if they had not been wounded, they would not have sought healing that resulted in a spiritual rebirth. Just as the phoenix dies and rises from its ashes, so might an individual be raised from their turmoil. Helichrysum lends its warrior spirit so that one may face their adversities with courage and determination. It brings hope to the most discouraged of souls and life to those in need of rebirth.

Negative Emotions: Intense pain, anguish, turmoil, hopeless, despair, trauma, wounded

Positive Properties: Healed, courageous, hopeful, transformation, perseverance, determination

JASMINE
The Oil of Sexual Purity & Balance

Jasmine nurtures healthy sexuality and helps to balance sexual forces. It may also arouse dormant passions, assisting individuals to regain interest in the sexual experience. Jasmine cultivates positive experiences within intimate relationships by encouraging the purification of unhealthy sexual intentions and motivations. It asks individuals to honor and respect themselves and others.

Jasmine encourages the release of past sexual trauma. Through its gentle, purifying nature, Jasmine brings forward unresolved sexual experiences and facilitates the healing process. Traumatic experiences can distort one's relationship with sexuality. Jasmine can assist both kinds of common compensations: those who fear, repel, or resist the sexual experience, as well as those who obsess over or are fixated with sexuality. It is balancing for individuals who use sex to fill a desperate need for love and approval, as well as individuals who resist sexual intimacy.

Jasmine supports the resolution of sexual trauma, encourages safety within intimate relationships, and invites only the purest intentions to the sexual experience.

Negative Emotions: Unresolved sexual trauma, resistance to sexuality, sexual fixation

Positive Properties: Healthy sexuality, pure intentions, innocent, healing, self-acceptance, intimate, trust, safety

JUNIPER BERRY
The Oil of Night

Juniper Berry assists those who fear the dark or unknown aspects of themselves. It helps individuals to understand that those things they fear are intended to be their teachers. Instead of hiding from what they do not understand, Juniper Berry encourages individuals to learn the lesson and face their fear. These fears often live within the unexplored areas of the Self. Juniper Berry acts as a catalyst by helping individuals access and address those fears and issues which have long been avoided.

Dreams contain nighttime communications. Even nightmares can reveal unresolved fears and issues. Juniper Berry offers courage and energetic protection in the nighttime. It encourages an honest assessment of the information being communicated from within.

As individuals reconcile with their fears and other hidden aspects of themselves, they experience greater wholeness. Juniper Berry helps restore the balance between light and dark, conscious and subconscious, day and night. It acts as a guide on the path toward wholeness. Juniper Berry teaches that there is truly nothing to fear when one acknowledges and accepts all aspects of the Self.

Negative Emotions: Irrational fears, recurrent nightmares, restless sleep

Positive Properties: Protected, dreaming, courageous, self-aware

LAVENDER
The Oil of Communication

Lavender aids verbal expression. It calms the insecurities that are felt when one risks their true thoughts and feelings. Lavender addresses a deep fear of being seen and heard. Individuals in need of Lavender hide within, blocking all forms of true self-expression. While they may even be going through the motions of outward expression, they're actually holding back their innermost thoughts and feelings. The expression is not connected to the heart or soul.

Lavender supports individuals in releasing the tension and constriction that stems from fear of expressing one's Self. Due to past experiences, they may believe it is not safe to express themselves. The True Self is therefore trapped within and goes unexpressed. Strong feelings of being unlovable, unimportant, or unheard can accompany this condition. The individual's fear of rejection paralyzes their true voice and traps their feelings inside.

Lavender encourages emotional honesty and insists that one speak their innermost thoughts and desires. As individuals learn to communicate their deepest thoughts and feelings, they are liberated from their self-inflicted prison. It is through open and honest communication that an individual experiences unconditional love and acceptance. Through Lavender's courageous spirit, one is free to share their True Self with others.

Negative Emotions: Blocked communication, fear of rejection, feeling unseen or unheard, constricted, tension, emotional dishonesty, hiding, fear of self-disclosure

Positive Properties: Open communication, relaxed, expressive, emotional honesty, heard

LEMON
The Oil of Focus

The delightful citrusy aroma of Lemon oil nourishes the mind and aids concentration. While Lemon supports the emotional body, its major effects are experienced in the mental field. The crisp scent of Lemon oil improves one's ability to focus. Lemon is a wonderful aid for children struggling with school. It teaches individuals to be mentally present by focusing on one thing at a time. Lemon dispels confusion and bestows clarity. It counterbalances mental fatigue due to too much studying or reading. Lemon restores energy, mental flexibility, and the drive to complete a project.

Lemon is especially helpful in cases of learning issues. Whether an individual has a difficult time concentrating or feels incapable of learning, Lemon clears self-judgments about learning such as "I'm dumb" or "I'm not a good student." Lemon calms fears and insecurities while restoring confidence in the Self.

Emotionally, Lemon inspires a natural playfulness and buoyancy in the heart. It assists in releasing feelings of despair and hopelessness by restoring feelings of joy and happiness. Lemon inspires joyful involvement in the present moment by infusing the soul with energy, confidence, and alertness.

Negative Emotions: Confusion, inability to focus, mental fatigue, lack of joy and energy, learning issues, guilt

Positive Properties: Focus, energy, mentally connected, alert, mental clarity, rational, joyful

LEMONGRASS
The Oil of Cleansing

Lemongrass is a powerful cleanser of energy. It dispels feelings of despondency, despair, and lethargy. Lemongrass assists individuals in entering a healing mode or cleansing state. In this state, one easily lets go of old, limiting beliefs, toxic energies, and negativity. Lemongrass teaches individuals to move forward without hesitation. It asks them to commit to a healing path where change is a regular occurrence.

Lemongrass can also be a powerful tool in cleansing the energy within a house, room, or office space. It encourages individuals with hoarding tendencies to courageously let go of everything they no longer need.

Lemongrass also clears negative energy from the brow chakra or spiritual eyes. As individuals let go of past issues and stagnant energy, they have an increased ability to see situations with greater clarity. It supports individuals' energy in flowing freely and smoothly. Lemongrass has a powerful mission to assist in cleansing physically, emotionally, and spiritually.

Negative Emotions: Toxic or negative energy, despair, holding on to the past, hoarding, darkness, spiritual blindness

Positive Properties: Clarity, cleansing, simplicity, discerning, letting go of past baggage

LIME
The Oil of Zest for Life

Lime imbues the soul with a zest for life. When an individual has been weighed down by discouragement or grief, Lime elevates them above the mire. It instills courage and cheer in the heart and reminds them to be grateful for the gift of life.

Lime cleanses the heart, especially when there has been an accumulation of emotional toxins due to avoidance or repression. This oil revitalizes the heart space, giving room for light and joy. It clears discouragement and thoughts and feelings related to a loss of will to live. Lime shines light on inner motives hidden in the heart and encourages emotional honesty.

Lime can also assist the individual who has overly developed their intellectual capacities but has neglected to develop themselves emotionally. This oil encourages balance between the heart and mind. It clears congestion from the heart region, assisting one in feeling safe and at home in their heart. Lime dispels apathy and resignation and instills hope, joy, courage, and the determination to face all of life's challenges.

Negative Emotions: Apathy, resignation, grief, loss of will to live, discouragement

Positive Properties: Courage, emotionally safe, engaged, revitalized, grateful for the gift of life, determined

MARJORAM
The Oil of Connection

Marjoram aids those who are unable to trust others or form meaningful relationships. This inability to trust often stems from harsh life experiences. The individual develops a fear of close connection in human relationships. They may tend toward reclusive behaviors, protecting themselves even further by abstaining from social interactions. They may also protect themselves by unconsciously sabotaging long-term relationships. Marjoram shows the barriers they have formed to protect themselves from others. It reveals patterns of aloofness, distancing one's self from other people, or being cold. Those in need of Marjoram oil most likely use these protective coping strategies unintentionally. Deep down they desire the intimate connection they subconsciously sabotage.

Marjoram teaches that trust is the basis for all human relationships. It assists an individual in increasing their warmth and trust in social situations. Marjoram softens the heart and heals past wounds. It kindles the fires of trust in relationships so that one may fully blossom. When an individual feels safe and loved, they express their authenticity more freely. Marjoram restores trust and openness so that true bonds of love may be formed in friendships and relationships.

Negative Emotions: Distrust, aloof, protected, distant, emotional isolation, reclusive, emotionally cold, fear of rejection

Positive Properties: Open, connected, close relationships, warm, softhearted, loving bonds, ability to trust, safe

MELALEUCA
The Oil of Energetic Boundaries

Disinfectant by nature, Melaleuca, also known as tea tree oil, clears negative energetic baggage. It specifically releases codependent and parasitic relationships. These toxic relationships may be with people, microorganisms in the physical body, or spiritual beings. The individual may feel drained of life force and energy, but they may not be consciously aware of the source of this energy leakage. Melaleuca helps break the negative ties in these kinds of relationships so that new, healthy connections may be formed that honor one's personal space and boundaries. This energetic "vampirism" between organisms violates the laws of nature. Melaleuca encourages an individual to connect to people and beings in ways that honor and respect others' agency. It helps the individual to recognize the parts of themselves that invited and allowed these kinds of relationships to exist in the first place.

Through these empowering processes, Melaleuca encourages an individual to relinquish all forms of self-betrayal, including allowing others to take advantage of one's time, energy, or talents; letting others feed on one's energy; not standing up for oneself; or feeling responsible for the problems of others. Melaleuca assists individuals in purification practices and in releasing toxic debris.

Negative Emotions: Parasitic and codependent relationships, poor boundaries, weak-willed, toxicity

Positive Properties: Energetic boundaries, respectful connections, empowered, resilient, honoring others' agency

MELISSA
The Oil of Light

Melissa oil awakens the soul to truth and light. It reminds individuals of who they truly are and why they came to this earth. Melissa invites one to release everything and anything that holds them back from reaching their fullest potential.

Melissa assists an individual in receiving spiritual guidance by reconnecting them with their inner voice. It uplifts the soul by literally preparing one to "uplevel." When an individual feels too weighed down by the burdens of life, Melissa encourages them to keep going. It gives strength and vitality to the innermost recesses of the heart and soul. This oil invites one to participate in higher realms of living and dreaming. As an individual stays connected to spiritual sources, they feel lightness in their being and brightness in their core. Melissa reminds everyone that each individual has a spark of divinity within them, and with love and attention, the spark will grow. This oil fuels that spark of energy, igniting an individual's True Self. Melissa assists them in shedding everything that is not in harmony with their inner light.

Melissa's enthusiasm is contagious. Through the intense light and vibration this oil has to offer, an individual may feel they cannot help but let go of feelings of darkness, despair, and other low vibrations that are holding them down. Melissa teaches one the joy of living.

Negative Emotions: Despair, hopeless, darkened, dreary, loss of will to live, overwhelmed

Positive Properties: Enlightened, joy of living, integrity, spiritual connection, contagious enthusiasm, liberated, optimistic

MYRRH
The Oil of Mother Earth

Myrrh oil nurtures the soul's relationship with its maternal mother and with the earth. This oil supports individuals who have had disturbances with the mother-child bond. Whether it's a division between the child and the biological mother or whether it's Mother Earth herself, Myrrh can help bridge the gap and heal the disturbance. This division or lack of attachment may be related to adoption, birth trauma, malnourishment, experiences of abandonment, or other childhood issues. Myrrh helps the soul to feel the love and nurturing presence of "mother." Similar to the nutrient-rich colostrum found in a mother's milk, Myrrh oil inoculates individuals from the adverse and harmful effects of the world. Like the warmth of a mother's love for her child, Myrrh assists individuals in feeling safe and secure.

When the mother-child bond has been disrupted, the soul may lose its childlike ability to trust. Feelings of trust are replaced with feelings of fear and a belief that the world is unsafe. Myrrh assists individuals in letting go of fear. Through reestablishing a healthy connection to the earth and to one's own mother, Myrrh rekindles trust within the soul. As the individual learns to once again live in trust, confidence in the goodness of life returns and the soul feels safer and more at home.

Negative Emotions: Disrupted maternal connection, distrust of others, feeling unsafe in the world, malnourished

Positive Properties: Feeling safe in the world, healthy attachments, trusting the goodness of life, bonded, maternal connection, nurtured, loved

OREGANO
The Oil of Humility & Nonattachment

Oregano cuts through the fluff of life and teaches individuals to do the same. It removes blocks, clears negativity, and cuts away negative attachments. Oregano is a powerful oil and may even be described as forceful or intense.

Oregano addresses a person's need to be right. The individual in need of Oregano may attempt to convert other people to their own fixed opinions. Their strong will can make them unteachable and unwilling to budge. They hold rigidly to their opinions and belief systems. However, Oregano is resolute and has the power to break through a strong will and teach humility.

On the deepest level, Oregano dispels materialism and attachment that hinders an individual's growth and progress. While using Oregano, a person may feel encouraged to end a toxic relationship, quit an oppressive job, or end a destructive habit. These toxic attachments limit one's capacity to feel a healthy connection to the Divine. Oregano encourages true spirituality by inviting the soul to live in nonattachment and teaches that devotion to a Higher Power includes letting go of rigidity, willfulness, negative attachments, and materialism.

Negative Emotions: Overly attached, pride, opinionated, negative, excessively willful, materialistic

Positive Properties: Humility, nonattachment, teachable, flexible, willingness to be wrong, devoted

PATCHOULI
The Oil of Physicality

Patchouli supports individuals in becoming fully present in their physical body. It balances those who feel devitalized and who seek to escape the body through spiritual pursuits or other forms of distraction. Patchouli tempers the obsessive personality by bringing them down to reality and teaching them moderation. This oil is grounding and stabilizing.

Patchouli compliments yoga practice, tai chi, or other exercises that aim to connect the spirit with the body. While using Patchouli, individuals feel more grounded and fluid. This oil calms fears and nervous tension, stilling the heart and mind in preparing the spirit and body for deeper union. It also helps individuals to stay in touch with the earth.

Patchouli helps individuals appreciate the magnificence of the physical body and all of its natural processes and functions. It assists in releasing emotional judgments and issues related to the body, such as believing the body is unholy or dirty. This oil helps with body image distortions and general body dislike. Patchouli brings confidence in the body, as well as grace, poise, and physical strength. It reminds individuals of their childhood experiences when they used their bodies for play and fun. On the deepest level, Patchouli assists an individual to feel at peace while being present in their physical body.

Negative Emotions: Body shame, disconnect from the body, judgment of the body, tension in the body

Positive Properties: Grounded, moderation, body contentment, balanced, stability, present, physically expressive

PEPPERMINT
The Oil of a Buoyant Heart

Peppermint brings joy and buoyancy to the heart and soul. It invigorates body, mind, and spirit and reminds individuals that life can be happy, and they don't have to be controlled by fear. It lifts an individual out of their emotional trials for a short reprieve. When an individual uses Peppermint, they feel as though they're gliding through life. It assists in staying on the surface of emotional issues like floating on top of water.

The power of Peppermint can be felt most in times of discouragement or despair. When the individual is disheartened, they may use Peppermint to rediscover the joy of being alive.

However, a person may also abuse the properties of Peppermint oil. If it is used as a permanent escape to avoid dealing with emotional pain, it can hinder growth and progress. Peppermint should not be used in this way. It aids individuals who need a short breather. At times, a reprieve is necessary before reentering emotional waters, but one is not meant to wade in the shallow end forever. When it is accepted and embraced, emotional pain serves as a teacher. Peppermint can assist an individual in regaining the strength needed to face their emotional reality.

Negative Emotions: Unbearable pain, intense despair, heaviness, pessimistic, muddled

Positive Properties: Buoyant, optimistic, clear, relieved, renewed, strength to face emotional pain

PETITGRAIN
The Oil of Ancestry

Petitgrain illuminates patterns and tendencies of unconsciously repeating family mistakes. The individual in need of Petitgrain is unable or unwilling to depart from their family's way of thinking. Instead, they follow in the footsteps of their predecessors and ancestral traditions. The individual feels a great sense of duty or loyalty towards their family's patterns and traditions. They view any departure from tradition as a betrayal of the family. They feel an obligation to continue carrying on the patterns and traditions whether they are healthy or not. In an attempt to honor their progenitors, the individual clings to old and accepted ways of thinking and being. Over time, the individual may even feel incapable of making different decisions.

Petitgrain invites individuals to make their own decisions, even if it means departing from conventional methods. It encourages a new, healthier connection between individuals and their families. Petitgrain supports individuals in making their own decisions in life while still feeling connected to their family and ancestry. It invokes a deep appreciation for positive forms of ancestral knowledge, wisdom, and family history. Petitgrain teaches that to actually honor one's family, one must live from their own center of truth.

Negative Emotions: Repeating negative family patterns, duty bound, inherited limitations, excessive loyalty to unhealthy traditions

Positive Properties: Balanced, pioneering, chain-breaking

ROMAN CHAMOMILE
The Oil of Spiritual Purpose

Roman Chamomile supports an individual in discovering and living their true life purpose. Regardless of what someone does for a living, they can find purpose and meaning in life with the help of this oil. As individuals live from the center of their beings, they find a power and a purpose that is indescribable. They feel calmer and more at peace. Roman Chamomile softens the personality, easing the overactive ego-mind. It restores one's confidence to do what they came to this earth to do. Like a guardian angel, Roman Chamomile leads the soul to where it needs to be and what it needs to be doing.

Roman Chamomile assists a person in shedding the meaningless activities that consume their lives so that they can focus on a more fulfilling work, even the work of their own souls. This oil assists in feeling connected to and supported by Divine helpers and guides, and calms insecurities about following one's spiritual path. People fear and believe that if they do what they love, they will end up destitute. Roman Chamomile says, "Do what you love to experience true success."

Negative Emotions: Purposeless, discouraged, drudgery, frustration, unsettled

Positive Properties: Purposeful, guided, peaceful, fulfilled, relaxed, Divine connection

ROSE
The Oil of Divine Love

Rose oil holds a higher frequency than any other oil on the planet. It is a powerful healer of the heart. It supports an individual in reaching heavenward and connecting with Divine love. Rose teaches the essential need for Divine grace and intervention in the healing process. As an individual opens to receive Divine benevolence in all its manifestations, the heart is softened. If one can simply let go and choose to receive Divine love, they are wrapped in warmth, charity, and compassion.

Rose invites individuals to experience the unwavering, unchanging, unconditional love of the Divine. This love heals all hearts and dresses all wounds. It restores an individual to authenticity, wholeness, and purity. As one feels unconditional love and acceptance, the heart is softened. As the heart fully opens, a fountain of love flows freely through the soul. In this state, one feels charity and compassion. Charity is experienced on behalf of oneself and others. Rose embodies Divine love and teaches individuals how to contact this love through prayer, meditation, and opening the heart to receive.

Negative Emotions: Bereft of Divine love, constricted feelings, closed or broken heart, lack of brotherly love

Positive Properties: Loved, compassionate, healed, tenderhearted, accepted, empathy, receiving Divine love

© Enlighten

ROSEMARY
The Oil of Knowledge & Transition

Rosemary assists in the development of true knowledge and true intellect. It teaches that one can be instructed from a far greater space of understanding than the human mind. It challenges individuals to look deeper than they normally would and ask more soul-searching questions so that they may receive more inspired answers.

Rosemary assists individuals who struggle with learning disabilities. It brings expansion to the mind, supporting individuals in receiving new information and new experiences.

Rosemary aids in times of transition and change. When a person is having a difficult time adjusting to a new house, school, or relationship, this oil can assist. Rosemary teaches that an individual does not understand all things because they have a mortal perspective. It invites individuals to trust in a higher, more intelligent power than themselves. It supports them in feeling confident and assured during times of great change in understanding or perspective. Rosemary roots them in the true knowledge that surpasses all understanding.

Negative Emotions: Confusion, difficulty adjusting or transitioning, ignorance, difficulties with learning

Positive Properties: Mental clarity, knowledgeable, teachable, inspired, open to new experiences

SANDALWOOD
The Oil of Sacred Devotion

Sandalwood assists with all kinds of prayer, meditation, and spiritual worship. It teaches reverence and respect for Deity. This oil has been used since ancient times for its powerful ability to calm the mind, still the heart, and prepare the spirit to commune with God.

Sandalwood teaches of spiritual devotion and spiritual sacrifice. It invites individuals to place all material attachments on the altar of sacrifice so that they may truly progress spiritually. This oil asks individuals to assess where their hearts are and challenges them to reorder their priorities to be in alignment with the Divine will.

Sandalwood assists in quieting the mind so that individuals may hear the subtle voice of the Spirit. It raises them into higher levels of consciousness. Sandalwood assists one in reaching beyond their current confines and belief systems. For those who are ready to leave behind attachment to fame, wealth, and the need for acceptance, Sandalwood teaches true humility, devotion, and love for the Divine.

Negative Emotions: Disconnected from God or spiritual Self, emptiness, overthinking, materialism

Positive Properties: Humility, spiritual devotion, spiritual clarity, stillness, surrender, higher consciousness

SPEARMINT
The Oil of Confident Speech

Spearmint inspires clarity of thought and confident verbal expression. The individual in need of Spearmint may hide their thoughts, opinions, and ideas by withholding their voice. Spearmint encourages inner clarity about one's personal convictions and opinions. It then assists individuals in translating that inner clarity into words.

Spearmint promotes confidence in expressing oneself verbally, especially when speaking in front of groups of people. It helps an individual create an effective stage presence by infusing an individual with confidence. Spearmint also encourages individuals to take a public stand on behalf of their values and opinions.

Spearmint can be a helpful remedy for those who struggle with communicating clearly for a wide range of reasons, from feeling scattered and inarticulate to stumbling over one's words. It assists individuals in becoming emotionally clear about what they want to say, and then saying it. In short, Spearmint can help individuals access their inner light and convey that light to the world with clarity and confidence.

Negative Emotions: Fear of public speaking, nervous, timid, afraid to express opinions

Positive Properties: Confidence, articulate speech, clarity, courage

SPIKENARD
The Oil of Gratitude

Spikenard encourages true appreciation for life. It addresses patterns of ingratitude, where individuals see themselves as the target of bad luck or a victim of their life circumstances. This perception can often lead to feelings of blame and anger. Spikenard encourages the soul to surrender and accept life exactly as it is. It invites individuals to let go and find an appreciation for all of life's experiences.

By opening the soul to acceptance and gratitude, Spikenard assists individuals in seeing the deeper meaning in their life. It supports them in feeling joy and happiness for other people as well as for themselves. It invites individuals to expand by fully letting go of resistance, anger, and blame.

Gratitude is an expression of complete acceptance. A grateful person is content with what they have. Spikenard teaches individuals to be grateful for their challenges as well as their blessings. It also assists individuals in transcending their sorrows through being grateful for their present life circumstances. Through complete surrender and acceptance, the soul may be brought into peace and harmony.

Negative Emotions: Ingratitude, resistance, victim mentality, greed, selfish, expecting bad luck

Positive Properties: Grateful, acceptance, content

© Enlighten

TANGERINE
The Oil of Cheer & Creativity

Tangerine's strong qualities of cheer and joyfulness can lift the darkest of moods. It can assist those who feel cut off from the lightness of heart often manifested by children. Those who feel overburdened by responsibility would benefit from Tangerine's uplifting vibration. It encourages a person to be creative and spontaneous.

Creativity can be stifled by an excessive sense of duty or creating rigid standards for oneself. While work, duty, and responsibility all have their place, feeling overworked, overly responsible, and overburdened leads to a loss of creative energy. Tangerine invites individuals to make room for their creative side, and asks that they reinsert fun, joy, and spontaneity into their lives.

Tangerine supports an individual in accessing the abundant pool of creative energy held within the spirit. It then assists that energy in flowing through the heart and into physical manifestation. Tangerine teaches the individual to enjoy life by being more abundantly creative and to reexperience the joy and cheerfulness they knew in childhood.

Negative Emotions: Overburdened by responsibilities, dutifulness which stifles creativity, downtrodden, heavyhearted, lack of fun or joy in life

Positive Properties: Cheerful, fun, abundantly creative, spontaneous, enjoying life, lighthearted, joyful, optimistic

THYME
The Oil of Releasing & Forgiving

Thyme is one of the most powerful cleansers of the emotional body and assists in addressing trapped feelings which have been buried for a long time. It reaches deep within the body and soul, searching for unresolved negativity. Thyme brings to the surface old, stagnant feelings. It is particularly helpful in treating the toxic emotions of hate, rage, anger, and resentment, which cause the heart to close.

Thyme empties the soul of all negativity, leaving the heart wide open. In this state of openness, an individual begins to feel tolerance and patience for others. As the heart opens more and more, it is able to receive love and offer forgiveness. Thyme teaches, "It's time to let go and move forward." As individuals forgive, they free themselves from emotional bondage. Thyme transforms hate and anger into love and forgiveness.

Negative Emotions: Unforgiving heart, anger, rage, hate, bitterness, resentment, emotional bondage

Positive Properties: Forgiving, tolerant, emotional release, patient, openhearted, understanding

VETIVER
The Oil of Centering & Descent

Vetiver oil assists in becoming more rooted in life. Life can scatter one's energy and cause one to feel split between different priorities, people, and activities. Vetiver brings the individual back down to earth. It assists them in grounding to the physical world. Vetiver also assists individuals in deeply connecting with what they think and feel. In this way, Vetiver is incredibly supportive in all kinds of self-awareness work. It helps uncover the root of an emotional issue.

Vetiver challenges an individual's need to escape their pain. It centers them in their True Self and guides them downward to the root of their emotional issues. It helps them find relief but not through avoidance. Relief comes after they have traveled within and met the core of their emotional issues. Vetiver will not let them quit. It grounds them in the present moment and carries them through an emotional catharsis. The descent into the Self assists individuals in discovering deeper facets of their being. Vetiver opens the doors to light and recovery through this downward journey.

Negative Emotions: Apathetic, despondent, disconnected, scattered, split, stressed, ungrounded, need to escape, crisis

Positive Properties: Centered, grounded, present, discovering deeper facets of being, emotionally connected, rooted

WHITE FIR
The Oil of Generational Healing

White Fir addresses generational issues. Patterns and traditions are passed down from family member to family member. Some of these patterns are positive while others are negative and destructive. Examples of negative patterns may include substance abuse, anger, codependency, physical or emotional abuse, eating issues, pride, and the need to be right.

White Fir assists the individual in unearthing these negative patterns from the hidden recesses of the body and soul. As they are brought to the light of consciousness, they can be dealt with and put to rest. The individual can choose not to participate in destructive family patterns and thereby break the tradition. White Fir aids this process and increases an individual's chances of success. In breaking these patterns, it offers a refuge of spiritual protection and helps individuals stay true to the path of healing, even if their family members oppose them in leaving behind their traditions.

Negative Emotions: Feelings that are generational or hereditary, burdened by the issues of others

Positive Properties: Free, generational healing, healthy patterns, creating new pathways, spiritual protection

WILD ORANGE
The Oil of Abundance

Wild Orange addresses a wide variety of emotional issues. It inspires abundance, fosters creativity, supports a positive mood, restores physical energy, and aids in transitions. Wild Orange also reconnects individuals with their inner child and brings spontaneity, fun, joy, and playfulness into one's life.

At its core, Wild Orange teaches the true meaning of abundance. It encourages individuals to let go of scarcity mindsets with all of their manifestations, including fear, nervousness, inflexibility, workaholism, lack of humor, and the belief that there is not enough. Wild Orange reminds the soul of the limitless supply found in nature. Fruit trees, like the orange tree, give freely to all in need. This oil teaches individuals to give without thought of compensation and encourages them to let go of their need to hoard, which is the epitome of scarcity.

Wild Orange also assists an individual's natural creative sense. It inspires limitless solutions for problems and issues. One never needs to fear. Wild Orange invites the individual to completely let go as a child does and to live from their authentic Self. In an individual's core, they are abundance. Sharing, playing, relaxing, and enjoying the bounties of life—these are the gifts bestowed by Wild Orange oil.

Negative Emotions: Scarcity, overserious, rigid, dull, workaholism, low energy, discouraged, hoarding, envy

Positive Properties: Abundant, humorous, playful, generous, spontaneous, creative, enjoying life

WINTERGREEN
The Oil of Surrender

Wintergreen is the oil of surrender. It can assist the strong-willed individual in letting go of the need to know and the need to be right. It takes great internal strength to surrender to a Higher Power. Wintergreen imbues the soul with this strength and teaches it how to let go and be free of the negativity and pain it holds on to. The belief that life is painful and must be shouldered alone makes it so. Wintergreen invites individuals to surrender these strong opinions.

Wintergreen reminds individuals that they not have to face life on their own. There is a constant invitation to surrender one's burdens to a Higher Power. All that is required is to release and let go. Wintergreen teaches that one can turn their hardships over to that Power greater than themselves so they do not have to carry the burden of life all alone.

Negative Emotions: Need to control, feeling weak, willful, need to be right, holding on, excessive self-reliance

Positive Properties: Surrender, letting go, teachable, inner strength, relying on the Divine

© Enlighten

YLANG YLANG
The Oil of the Inner Child

Ylang Ylang is a powerful remedy for the heart. Modern day society honors and reveres the mind over the heart. Yet the heart, with its intuitive ways of receiving information, is an essential part of the soul. Ylang Ylang reconnects an individual with the inner child and the pure, simple ways of the heart. It encourages play and restores a childlike nature and innocence. It assists in accessing intuition or "heart knowing."

Ylang Ylang is also a powerful remedy for releasing emotional trauma from the past. It is a fantastic support in age regression work and other methods of emotional healing. Ylang Ylang also assists individuals in releasing bottled-up emotions such as anger and sadness. Feelings that have been buried are brought to light through Ylang Ylang's assistance. This oil allows emotional healing to flow naturally, nurturing the heart through the process. It reminds the individual that joy can be felt and experienced more fully by allowing the heart its full range of emotions.

Negative Emotions: Joyless, overstressed, grief, sadness, loss of a loved one, disconnected from inner child

Positive Properties: Freedom, playful, intuitive, heart healing, emotionally filled, joyful, accepting

OIL BLENDS

INTRODUCTION TO OIL BLENDS

How to Find Your Favorite Blend

We have not used any trademark names in the Oil Blends section. However, most blends are listed by their subtitle name and can be found by looking at the essential oil bottle. For example, if the blend you are looking for is Breathe, then the subtitle is Respiratory Blend in this book.

About Oil Blends

Oil blends are created by combining several single oils to form an entirely new product. Blends are formulated to address a specific physical or emotional theme or issue. Oil blends are different from single oils but not necessarily superior. Still, blends may be more equipped than single oils in some ways. When formulated well, oil blend create synergies, or increased effectiveness, in supporting the specific issues they were created to address.

Emotional Aromatherapy Blends

Six blends in this section have been labeled Emotional Aromatherapy Blends. These blends have been specially formulated to assist individuals in balancing their moods and working through their emotions. Each of these blends utilize the emotional properties of two aromatic plant families and target six unique emotional states.

ANTI-AGING BLEND
The Oil of Spiritual Insight

Essential oils have been used since antiquity to assist meditation practices, prayer, and spiritual worship. Anti-Aging Blend combines the power of high vibrational oils alongside grounding oils to assist the connection between spirit and body, heaven and earth. This blend encourages positive states of being and supports the development of faith, hope, gratitude, kindness, love, patience, and trust in the Divine.

Anti-Aging Blend is a wonderful aid for meditation as it quiets the mind, fosters inner stillness and encourages spiritual growth. While this oil is gentle, it is also very powerful. It assists the release of negativity, darkness, and limiting perceptions. Anti-Aging Blend can mitigate spiritual blindness and other spiritual issues by offering profound light to individuals.

Anti-Aging Blend offers grace and comfort when one feels discouraged or distressed. This oil can assist individuals in transcending the darkness, pain, and stresses of life. At its core, Anti-Aging Blend offers support in raising levels of human consciousness and preparing individuals for new heights of spiritual transformation.

Ingredients: Frankincense, Sandalwood, Lavender, Myrrh, and other essential oils

Negative Emotions: Dark night of the soul, spiritual blindness, burdened, discouraged

Positive Properties: Hope, spiritual transformation, faith, trust in the Divine, higher consciousness, stillness

CLEANSING BLEND
The Oil of Purification

Cleansing Blend assists individuals in releasing toxic emotions and entering a cleansing state. It revitalizes the energy system, washing away negative influences. This blend supports individuals who feel trapped by negativity or toxicity. Cleansing Blend provides freedom from past habits and patterns. It is especially helpful in combating toxic feelings of hate, rage, and enmeshment and in severing other negative attachments.

Like Lemongrass, Cleansing Blend makes a wonderful space cleanser. It can clear negative energy from the household and the environment, as well as cleanse the air of odor and harmful microorganisms. Diffused in the air, this oil can facilitate emotional breakthroughs. In order to heal, one must receive. But in order to receive, one must first release what is blocking the new, clean energy from entering. Cleansing Blend supports individuals in constantly releasing the old so they may be open to the new.

Ingredients: Lemon, Lime, Pine, Citronella, and other essential oils

Negative Emotions: Trapped, stuck, hate, rage, control, negative attachments

Positive Properties: Unencumbered, clean, refreshed, purified, emotional breakthroughs

COMFORTING BLEND

The Oil of Consolation

Emotional Aromatherapy Blend

This blend of trees and flowers was formulated to assist individuals who are in need of emotional comfort. It soothes emotional pain after periods of extreme stress or trauma. Comforting Blend assists individuals who are burdened by loss, grief, or tragedy. When past emotional hurts resurface, Comforting Blend can assist in releasing these emotional burdens.

When a storm is raging in one's heart or mind, or when there is no relief from fear, emotional pain, or anxious feelings, Comforting Blend can assist individuals in taking the first steps toward healing. It encourages individuals to seek Divine intervention so they may experience the ever-present mantle of warmth, love, and consolation. Comforting Blend helps ease one's burdens, assists in experiencing a serene heart and mind, and guides individuals toward emotional rest.

Ingredients: Frankincense, Patchouli, Ylang Ylang, Labdanum, Amyris, Sandalwood, and other essential oils

Negative Emotions: Grief, loss, traumatized, anxious, restless, unsettled, emotional pain, burdened

Positive Properties: Comforted, content, restful, whole, serene

DETOXIFICATION BLEND
The Oil of Vitality & Transition

Detoxification Blend is designed to cleanse the organs and systems of the body. Emotionally, this blend assists during times of transition and change. It can assist an individual in "detoxing" old habits and limiting beliefs. When an individual has felt trapped by self-sabotaging behaviors, Detoxification Blend paves the way for new life experiences. It aids in letting go of behaviors that are destructive to one's health and happiness. It is especially helpful during major life changes which require adjustments in habit and lifestyle, such as altering diet, quitting smoking, or leaving a toxic relationship.

Detoxification Blend reawakens vital life energy. It also assists an individual in discovering new energy and vitality by encouraging the release of physical and emotional toxins. This blend aids in shedding apathy as well as any destructive habit, helping a person find new enthusiasm for life. As individuals let go of limiting beliefs, behaviors, and lifestyles, they have greater room to receive. As a result, they are able to see life from a fresh perspective and embrace new experiences.

Ingredients: Tangerine, Rosemary, Geranium, and other essential oils

Negative Emotions: Difficulty with transitions, toxic habits, limiting beliefs, apathy

Positive Properties: Unrestricted, revitalized, clear, embracing new experiences

DIGESTIVE BLEND
The Oil of Digestion

The Digestive Blend was formulated to support the body's digestive system. It also has a powerful emotional quality for supporting individuals who lack interest in life and the physical world. The individual may have a tendency to take on too much at once. This overload of information and stimulation may lead to an emotional form of "indigestion," where the individual cannot break down life experiences into palatable forms. The soul literally becomes overfed and undernourished, as it cannot translate its experiences into a usable form. When the individual is overwhelmed and overstimulated, they may lose their appetite for food, life, and the physical world in general. They may become apathetic about their situation and begin neglecting their body's basic needs.

Digestive Blend combines the powerful oils of Ginger, Peppermint, and other spices to support the body and the spirit in assimilating new information and events. It increases an individual's ability to receive new information, new relationships, and new experiences and be open to new possibilities. This blend powerfully aids individuals in digesting life's many experiences.

Ingredients: Ginger, Peppermint, Tarragon, Fennel, Caraway, and other essential oils

Negative Emotions: Loss of appetite for food or life, inability to assimilate new information or experiences, overstimulated

Positive Properties: Enthusiasm, nourished, interested, assimilating new information and events

DNA REPAIRING BLEND

The Oil of Transformation

DNA Repairing Blend works emotionally as well as physically with the cycles of life and death and personal transformation. By putting off the old, we become free to experience the new—this is transformation. DNA Repairing Blend supports the body's sick or damaged cells to either transition to death, or to transform, repair, and renew. Through the help and support of this blend, individuals can assist their bodies, cells, energy, and emotions in returning to a balanced, healthy, and authentic state.

DNA Repairing Blend is particularly supportive in releasing all types of negative family patterns which are recorded in the body itself (in the DNA). It is especially suited for those who struggle with debilitating circumstances, as it helps to relieve feelings of doubt, disbelief, despair, and burden. It teaches individuals to reclaim their life energy and to believe that change is possible. DNA Repairing Blend supports the process of regaining health and vitality by encouraging the release of the old and the birth of the new.

Ingredients: Frankincense, Wild Orange, Lemongrass, Thyme, Summer Savory, and other essential oils

Negative Emotions: Debilitated, discouraged, toxic, stuck, burdened by family patterns

Positive Properties: Repaired, balanced, transformation, rebirth, vitality, healthy, open to change

ENCOURAGING BLEND

The Oil of Motivation

Emotional Aromatherapy Blend

This blend of mints and citrus oils was formulated for those who need motivation and encouragement. It assists individuals whose will has stagnated and needs to be fired into action again. Encouraging Blend fosters confidence to follow through with one's creative inspirations and intentions. It also imbues a warrior-like spirit and strengthens one to face adversities and challenges.

This blend is especially helpful in times of weariness and discouragement when one has lost the energy and motivation to complete important life tasks, such as caring for a sick loved one or assisting others in need. It is easy to become lethargic or discouraged when one is in a long-term care situation or another emotionally or physically taxing circumstance. Encouraging Blend can act as a support in rediscovering and maintaining one's desire to serve. It encourages individuals to work through their feelings of gloom, weariness, or hopelessness, rather than slipping into despondency or despair. Instead of remaining paralyzed by these feelings, this blend launches individuals into positive action. It confidently reassures that they do have the courage needed to face another day.

Ingredients: Peppermint, Clementine, Coriander, Basil, Yuzu, Melissa, and other essential oils

Negative Emotions: Weary, discouraged, stagnant, gloomy, lacking motivation, unable to press on

Positive Properties: Motivated, encouraged, hopeful, energized, confident

79

FOCUS BLEND
The Oil of Presence

In contrast to Lemon oil, known as "The Oil of Focus," Focus Blend calms the mind, facilitating inner peace. Whereas Lemon activates the mind, Focus Blend quiets and grounds mental forces. It is especially beneficial to those with a short attention span. It encourages individuals to remain present with the task at hand and to complete a project, goal, or activity before moving onto the next. Focus Blend is therefore supportive to individuals who become lost in thought—those who rapidly jump from one activity or idea to the next—as well as those who lose themselves in daydreams or fantasy.

Focus Blend gently guides the soul into full awareness of its physical body and physical surroundings. It invites individuals to accept the reality of their life situation, so they may deal with it appropriately. This blend especially encourages individuals to live in the here and now, and therefore promotes a meditative state. Focus Blend's stability and grounding energy supports a healthy connection between the body and the mind. With the support of Focus Blend, individuals are empowered to live fully connected in the present moment.

Ingredients: Amyris, Patchouli, Frankincense, Lime, Ylang Ylang, and other essential oils

Negative Emotions: Distraction, lack of physical presence or awareness, daydreaming, procrastination, scattered

Positive Properties: Focused, completion of projects and tasks, living in the present moment, calm, grounded

GROUNDING BLEND
The Oil of Grounding

Grounding Blend is primarily a combination of tree oils and roots. Trees live in the present moment. They are not in a hurry. They are stable. Grounding Blend's soft energy is excellent for calming overactive children who have difficulty settling down. It is also a wonderful remedy for adults who need to reconnect with their roots. Grounding Blend strengthens a connection with the lower body and with the earth. These connections are especially important when the upper faculties have been overused due to excessive thinking, speaking, or spiritual activity.

Grounding Blend is especially suited for personalities who seek to escape from life through disconnection or disassociation. These individuals may avoid long-term commitments in work or relationships, preferring instead to drift. This blend reminds individuals that to realize their true dreams and desires, they must stay focused on a goal until it is actualized in the physical world. Grounding Blend teaches true perseverance by assisting the individual in staying present with a specific plan or idea until it is embodied. Providing inner strength and fortitude, Grounding Blend teaches individuals to ground their energy and to manifest their vision with the patience of a tree.

Ingredients: Spruce, Ho Wood, Frankincense, and other essential oils

Negative Emotions: Ungrounded, unwilling to take responsibility for self or life, disconnected, unstable, scattered

Positive Properties: Body connection, stability, perseverance, self-contained, grounded, inner strength

INSPIRING BLEND

The Oil for Finding Your Passion

Emotional Aromatherapy Blend

This blend of spices and herbs was formulated to assist individuals who are lacking inner passion. It is helpful for those caught in patterns of self-denial or regimentation. Overworking and being too serious can dull one's sensitivity and emotions. When individuals are burdened by a joyless sense of duty, Inspiring Blend encourages them to be more playful and spontaneous. It teaches that there is more to living than working and obligation.

When appropriate, Inspiring Blend encourages individuals to take risks, to confidently face their fears, and to break free from the limitations they place on themselves. It challenges individuals to use their creativity and imagination to fulfill their true life's passions. In short, when life has become a dull set of routines and obligations, Inspiring Blend acts as a reminder to rediscover one's inner passion.

Ingredients: Cardamom, Cinnamon, Ginger, Clove, Sandalwood, Jasmine, and other essential oils

Negative Emotions: Self-denial, regimented, dutiful, serious, dull, joyless, burdened

Positive Properties: Passionate, risk-taking, vitality, inspired, alive, playful, spontaneous, creative

INVIGORATING BLEND
The Oil of Creativity

Invigorating Blend acts as a powerful "fire starter." It returns motivation and drive when it is lacking. This is a wonderful combination of oils for addressing lethargy, discouragement, despondency, or a low will to live. When the soul has lost its connection to the magic in life, this blend helps restore the spark.

Invigorating Blend also inspires creativity. Every human soul has a need to create. These oils inspire creative expression by reconnecting individuals with their inner child and their natural creative sense. They assist individuals in living abundantly and spontaneously by encouraging play and excitement. Invigorating Blend can motivate individuals to use their true creative power by letting go of old limitations and insecurities. It takes courage to put oneself out there artistically. Citruses in particular bring color and imagination to one's life. Placed over the solar plexus, this combination of oils restores confidence in one's Self and in one's creations. Invigorating Blend rekindles the fire in the personality and fills the heart with creativity and joy.

Ingredients: Wild Orange, Lemon, Grapefruit, Mandarin, Bergamot, Tangerine, and other essential oils

Negative Emotions: Stifled or blocked creativity, fear of self-expression, emotionally imbalanced, low will to live

Positive Properties: Invigorated, childlike, creative, motivated, cheerful, self-expression, spontaneous

JOYFUL BLEND
The Oil of Joy

Joyful Blend is formulated to overcome feelings of despair and hopelessness. This blend combines powerful mood-stabilizing oils with joy-filled oils that evoke happiness. The warm vibrations of these oils can soothe the heart and balance emotions.

Joyful Blend can assist individuals in letting go of lower energy vibrations. Negative habits lose their appeal as an individual shifts into higher levels of consciousness. This blend can raise one's energy levels and energetic vibrations into higher states. It can inspire feelings of cheerfulness, brightness, courage, relaxation, happiness, humor, playfulness and fun. By inspiring these feelings, Joyful Blend transforms despair into sunshine and joy. It teaches that worry and fear are not productive, but faith, hope, and determination are. Joyful Blend powerfully persuades people to be happy, carefree, and abundant. It supports individuals in flowing with life while remaining in peace and light.

Ingredients: Lavandin, Tangerine, Elemi, Lemon Myrtle, Melissa, Ylang Ylang, and other essential oils

Negative Emotions: Caught in low vibrations, despair, dark, serious, stern

Positive Properties: Brightness, joy, carefree, humor, elevated, courage, cheerfulness, abundant, sunny disposition

MASSAGE BLEND
The Oil of Relaxation

Massage Blend assists the body in calming, relaxing, and releasing physical tension. On an emotional level, Massage Blend moves an individual from stiffness of heart and mind to openness and flexibility. This Blend is soothing to both body and mind and offers comfort in times of grief and sorrow.

Most people seek out massage when they are tense or stressed. Through bodywork and massage, the individual is able to relax their tight muscles. Breathing may begin to regulate, slow, and deepen. As an individual's body relaxes, so does their mind. As the muscles release tension, the heart can reopen to life. Circulation is enhanced, as is the ability to move with life and allow things to flow. This is the gift of the Massage Blend—the ability to relax, open, and move in harmony once more with the body and with existence.

Ingredients: Basil, Grapefruit, Cypress, Marjoram, and other essential oils

Negative Emotions: Tense, stiffness in body or mind, stressed, unable to relax

Positive Properties: Relaxed, harmonious, flexible, openness of heart and mind, comforted

METABOLIC BLEND

The Oil of Inner Beauty

In addition to supporting the physical aspects of weight loss, this blend may also be used to address the emotional patterns which underlie and contribute to one's weight. Individuals in need of Metabolic Blend may set strict standards for themselves in diet or weight loss programs. They believe that by denying themselves of dietary pleasures and controlling their bodies, they will force their desired result. Instead, their punitive withholding is met with whiplash from the body as it desperately seeks to survive. The need for foods and sweets becomes excessive, resulting in swings in diet, weight, and mood. This usually causes discouragement and feeling out of control, as one berates themselves with criticism and self-hatred.

The Metabolic Blend can support individuals in releasing the heavy emotions which contribute to physical and emotional pounds. It encourages them to find feelings of self-worth. As they accept their body as it is, the body can more easily move towards its ideal expression. Metabolic Blend encourages individuals to rise above self-judgment by embracing the body's natural beauty and inherent value, regardless of weight, shape, or size.

Ingredients: Grapefruit, Lemon, Peppermint, and other essential oils

Negative Emotions: Self-criticism, worthlessness, feeling ugly, disgust or hate for physical appearance

Positive Properties: Worthwhile, embracing the body's individual beauty, self-acceptance, inherent value

MONTHLY BLEND
The Oil of Vulnerability

Monthly Blend encourages warmth in relationships, stabilizes emotional imbalances, and fosters emotional intimacy. It is a perfect blend for supporting pregnancy and child delivery, as it strengthens the mother-child bond. This blend assists women in accepting their maternal instincts and nurturing qualities.

Monthly Blend assists relationships by teaching individuals to be emotionally open and vulnerable. It eases the fear of rejection and encourages individuals to receive true warmth and love in their relationships. It also encourages feelings of empathy for others by reminding them to stay receptive to the thoughts, feelings, and needs of other people.

This blend works as a powerful emotional stabilizer, especially during menstruation or menopause. It releases emotional tension within the reproductive organs and helps release the expectations of suffering and dread related to the monthly cycle. In short, Monthly Blend encourages emotional intimacy and assists individuals in emotional balancing.

Ingredients: Clary Sage, Lavender, Bergamot, Roman Chamomile, Cedarwood, Ylang Ylang, Geranium, Fennel, Carrot Seed, and other essential oils

Negative Emotions: Invulnerability, guarded, closed, dread of menstruation or menopause

Positive Properties: Vulnerable, empathy, bonding, warmth, solace, emotional intimacy

PROTECTIVE BLEND
The Oil of Protection

This combination of oils is generally used to shield individuals from bacteria, mold, and viruses. This blend's protective properties, however, extend beyond the physical level by aiding individuals in warding off energetic parasites, domineering personalities, and other negative influences. The Protective Blend strengthens one's immune system, which governs the ability to defend against attacks from physical pathogens and negative energies.

Protective Blend is incredibly helpful for strengthening the inner Self along with the inner resolve to stand up for one's Self and live in integrity. This blend is especially indicated for personalities who have a weakened boundary due to some kind of perpetual violation to their personal space. Protective Blend gives individuals strength to say "no" and resolve to maintain clear boundaries. It cuts away unhealthy connections such as codependency, parasitic relationships, or emotional viruses found in negative "group thought." Protective Blend greatly assists individuals in learning to stand up for themselves and live in integrity with their True Self.

Ingredients: Wild Orange, Clove, Cinnamon, and other essential oils

Negative Emotions: Attacked, unprotected, vulnerable, susceptibility to peer pressure

Positive Properties: Protected, capable, boundaries, integrity, independent, reinforced, strength

REASSURING BLEND

The Oil of Peace

Emotional Aromatherapy Blend

This blend of flowers and mints was formulated to assist individuals who lack inner peace. All people thrive when they feel connected to the Divine. Souls achieve true and lasting peace through connection to this source. Without this true peace, there is a human tendency to try to manufacture peace by controlling one's environment and relationships. Especially when one feels afraid, it is tempting to try to control others because it gives an artificial sense of order and safety.

Reassuring Blend invites individuals to connect to the true source of unending peace and let go of control and excess attachments in order to experience the incredible peace that flows from the Divine. It invites us to trust in Divine goodness and grace. Reassuring Blend affirms that no amount of control or effort can fill the empty soul. It reminds individuals that only by connecting to the Divine will can they cultivate lasting peace.

Ingredients: Vetiver, Lavender, Ylang Ylang, Frankincense, Clary Sage, Marjoram, and other essential oils

Negative Emotions: Controlling, attached, afraid

Positive Properties: Peaceful, serene, content, still

RENEWING BLEND

The Oil of Forgiving

Emotional Aromatherapy Blend

This blend of herb and tree oils was formulated to assist individuals who desire to forgive. It is well understood that forgiving others actually sets us free. This blend is especially helpful when individuals feel cynical or begin to expect the worst from other people. Instead of looking for the good in others, they may view others in a negative light. They may also have a tendency to feel justified in blaming others for their own personal situations or misfortunes. Renewing Blend teaches that everyone is learning and growing together. Mistakes and offenses will certainly happen but should be met with forgiveness and kindness.

Renewing Blend challenges individuals to let go of bitterness and hostilities and to embrace other people as an extension of themselves, as part of the human family. It reminds individuals to live by the Golden Rule—to treat others the way they themselves would like to be treated. It invites individuals to free themselves by realizing that others are usually doing the best they can and deserve our compassion and forgiveness.

Ingredients: Spruce, Bergamot, Juniper Berry, Myrrh, Arborvitae, Nootka Tree, and other essential oils

Negative Emotions: Critical, judgmental, resentful, cynical, bitter, blaming, angry

Positive Properties: Forgiving, light, free, loving, understanding, tolerant

REPELLENT BLEND
The Oil of Shielding

Repellent Blend was formulated as an insect repellent, but it also offers so much more. This blend helps individuals to stay calm in the face of danger or attack. Repellent Blend strengthens the protective shield around one's body, helping them to feel safe. This is especially important for children and adults who unconsciously merge with other people's energy. They may do this as a way to relieve others' burdens or to simply lighten the load in the environment. Regardless of the motives, this type of energetic merging weakens an individual's energy system. Babies and young children are especially susceptible to trying to carry loved ones' feelings for them, as they struggle to know which emotions are theirs and which belong to other people. This blend can assist an individual in separating their own energy from another's.

While the confusion between boundaries is often unintentional, there are also those who would target or attack another person. Repellent Blend teaches individuals to hold strong boundaries and not allow themselves to be pushed around. It imbues individuals with courage and confidence to stand up for themselves and face their attackers.

Ingredients: Lemon, Eucalyptus, Citronella, and other essential oils

Negative Emotions: Unprotected, attacked, defenseless, poor boundaries

Positive Properties: Courage, standing up for self, self-contained, safe, strong boundaries

RESPIRATORY BLEND
The Oil of Breath

Respiratory Blend addresses the inability to let go of grief and pain. The individual in need of Respiratory Blend struggles to breathe and literally feels suffocated by sadness. The lungs and air passages become constricted, preventing air and emotion from releasing. The root of this condition is feeling unloved; the individual grieves the love they never received. They often shut down due to fear, not knowing whether the love they need will be there. They distrust whether it's safe to open and take in life. Respiratory Blend encourages individuals to release grief and sadness and to receive genuine love and healing.

Respiratory Blend also supports an individual's relationship with Spirit and deepens one's connection to life. It invites individuals to let go (breathe out) and receive (breathe in). In this way, this blend teaches individuals to embrace life through breath. Respiratory Blend imbues individuals with the courage to fully open.

Ingredients: Laurel Leaf (Bay), Peppermint, Eucalyptus, Melaleuca, and other essential oils

Negative Emotions: Sadness, grief, despair, unloved, difficulty breathing, constriction, distrust

Positive Properties: Loved, cared for, receiving, courage to fully open, embracing life, healed, solace

RESTFUL BLEND
The Oil of Tranquility

Restful Blend has a powerful effect on the mind and heart. It is a uniquely calming blend that invites individuals to relinquish feelings of stress, anxiousness, and being overwhelmed. Restful Blend can support those who struggle with an overactive mind and inability to unwind. From feelings of responsibility to feelings of worry, Restful Blend assists in quieting the mind, releasing agitation and inviting calm.

When individuals over-identify with responsibilities or fears, they create emotional states that do not support proper rest, relaxation, and rejuvenation. Driven by constant pressures and perceived burdens, individuals struggle to keep up with the demands of their lives. This blend powerfully addresses the underlying states that are often the cause of restlessness, stress, and imbalance.

Restful Blend encourages individuals to first reconnect with themselves and discover the peace that lies within, then to reconnect with the humanity in others. It invites individuals to acknowledge when they feel out of balance and allow time and space for true renewal. It also gently reminds that others are often caught in similar cycles of imbalance and encourages compassion and acceptance of them. Restful Blend brings a sense of tranquility that allows space for personal reflection, peace, and healing.

Ingredients: Lavender, Marjoram, Roman Chamomile, Ylang Ylang, Cedarwood, Vetiver and other essential oils

Negative Emotions: Stress, emotional overload, agitation, restlessness, anxiousness, disconnected

Positive Properties: Calm, tranquil, peaceful, relaxed, compassionate, connected

SKIN CLEARING BLEND
The Oil of Accepting Imperfections

Skin-Clearing Blend was formulated for acne and general skin health. Its major ingredient, Black Cumin seed, is not an essential oil, but has trace amounts of essential oil within it. Black Cumin is prized in many Islamic countries for its healing properties. Skin-Clearing Blend combines the healing properties of Black Cumin with other essential oils.

Skin-Clearing Blend emotionally supports suppressed anger, guilt, and self-judgment. The individual in need of this blend may harbor feelings of guilt or anger from the past. These deeply buried feelings may exist outside the individual's conscious awareness. Yet these feelings of pain or anger literally "boil" to the surface. If the individual does not deal with these feelings appropriately, they may manifest through lashing out or blaming others.

Skin-Clearing Blend supports individuals by increasing self-acceptance and self-love. It assists them in seeing their inherent worth, regardless of physical appearance. It encourages the healthy release and expression of feelings of anger. Skin-Clearing Blend invites individuals to look past menial imperfections and to replace self-judgment with self-acceptance.

Ingredients: Black Cumin Seed, Ho Wood, Melaleuca, Litsea Berry, and other essential oils

Negative Emotions: Pain, anger, self-judgment

Positive Properties: Self-acceptance, self-love, worthwhile, personal responsibility

SOOTHING BLEND
The Oil of Surrendering Pain

Soothing Blend is generally used for physical pain, but it can also assist individuals who are resisting or avoiding the emotions that underlie their physical pain. It gives a person strength to face their emotional wounds, allowing the wounds to surface for transformation and healing. This blend can teach individuals how to be the observer of their painful experiences rather than overidentifying with them. When a person suffers from intense emotional or physical pain, it is common for them to act irrationally or lose their head. Soothing Blend can support the mind in staying cool and collected, regardless of the emotional turmoil or physical pain one may be in. In this way, the individual maintains mental clarity in the face of danger or pain.

At its core, Soothing Blend teaches individuals acceptance and tolerance of their pain. It reveals the possibility that pain is not cruel or bad but is simply a teacher. Instead of resisting pain, one may embrace the lessons it has to offer. As one lets go of resistance, pain lessens and often dissipates altogether. By understanding the nature of pain, this blend encourages an assimilation of all life's experiences.

Ingredients: Wintergreen, Camphor, Peppermint, Blue Tansy, Blue Chamomile, and other essential oils

Negative Emotions: Resistance to pain, avoidance of emotional issues, hysteria in painful situations

Positive Properties: Strength, accepting painful experiences, soothed, serene, cool-headed, embracing

TENSION BLEND
The Oil of Relief

Formulated to relieve headaches, Tension Blend also assists individuals in releasing the stress and emotional tension that may have contributed to or caused their headache.

Tension Blend synergistically combines the powerful relaxation qualities of essential oils to assist and teach the body how to calm and relax. It can also help individuals release the fears that create tension and pain in the physical body. Tension Blend can calm severe stress, soothe trauma, and bring balance to the body and energy system. This blend also helps in regaining equilibrium following periods of overwork, burnout, and fatigue.

As physical and emotional discomforts are relieved, Tension Blend fosters feelings of appreciation. It reminds individuals to be grateful for and enjoy their many life experiences.

Ingredients: Wintergreen, Lavender, Peppermint, Frankincense, Cilantro, Roman Chamomile, Marjoram, and other essential oils

Negative Emotions: Stress, overworked, nervous, burnout, overwhelmed, fatigued

Positive Properties: Calm, relaxed body and mind, equilibrium, relieved, grateful

UPLIFTING BLEND

The Oil of Cheer

Emotional Aromatherapy Blend

This blend of citrus and spices was formulated to assist individuals who are in need of cheerfulness. It is especially helpful for individuals who feel heavyhearted or who have been weighed down by many challenges in life. Encountering repeated trials over an extended period of time can have crippling effects, and may even create an expectation of permanent suffering with no hope of relief.

Uplifting Blend encourages individuals who are overcome by feelings of hopelessness and helplessness. It helps restore one's hope when they have been stretched beyond the limits of their endurance. This blend inspires faith that life will work out for the best despite difficulties and setbacks. Uplifting Blend reminds individuals there is so much more to life than the hardship they are experiencing, and to determinedly hold on until they regain the hope and joy they feel they've lost.

Ingredients: Wild Orange, Clove, Star Anise, Lemon Myrtle, Zdravetz, Nutmeg, Vanilla, and other essential oils

Negative Emotions: Burdened, hopeless, joyless, heavyhearted, helpless

Positive Properties: Hopeful, comforted, faithful, cheerful, uplifted, joyful, determined

WOMEN'S BLEND
The Oil of Femininity

The benefits of Women's Blend are not limited to women alone. While this blend possesses a strong feminine quality, its female energy is often needed by both men and women.

Women's Blend softens the overly masculine individual by getting them in touch with their feminine side. It encourages individuals to let go of pride and let down their tough exterior. When placed over the liver, Women's Blend can ease feelings of anger. It calms tension, irritability, and malice, and encourages adaptability.

Women's Blend assists individuals in healing their relationships with their mothers, grandmothers, and other women. It helps one reconnect with their mother when there has been strain, separation, loss, or abuse in the relationship. It challenges an individual to work through their issues relating to both femininity and sexuality. If one has rejected their feminine energy, this blend invites them to heal their wounds and find balance by reconnecting with their feminine side.

Ingredients: Patchouli, Bergamot, Sandalwood, Rose, Jasmine, Cinnamon, Cistus, Vetiver, Ylang Ylang, and other essential oils

Negative Emotions: Overly masculine, blocked or imbalanced female energy, unteachable, anger, irritable, tough exterior

Positive Properties: Humility, kindness, softened, acceptance of feminine, teachable, adaptable

SECTION III

APPENDICES

APPENDIX A

Essential Oils List

SINGLE OILS

1. Arborvitae
2. Basil
3. Bergamot
4. Birch
5. Black Pepper
6. Cardamom
7. Cassia
8. Cedarwood
9. Cilantro
10. Cinnamon
11. Clary Sage
12. Clove
13. Coriander
14. Cypress
15. Dill
16. Douglas Fir
17. Eucalyptus
18. Fennel
19. Frankincense
20. Geranium
21. Ginger
22. Grapefruit
23. Helichrysum
24. Jasmine
25. Juniper Berry
26. Lavender
27. Lemon
28. Lemongrass
29. Lime
30. Marjoram
31. Melaleuca
32. Melissa
33. Myrrh
34. Oregano
35. Patchouli
36. Peppermint
37. Roman Chamomile
38. Petitgrain
39. Rose
40. Rosemary
41. Sandalwood
42. Spearmint
43. Spikenard
44. Tangerine
45. Thyme
46. Vetiver
47. White Fir
48. Wild Orange
49. Wintergreen
50. Ylang Ylang

OIL BLENDS

1. Anti-Aging Blend
2. Cleansing Blend
3. Comforting Blend
4. Detoxification Blend
5. Digestive Blend
6. DNA Repairing Blend
7. Encouraging Blend
8. Focus Blend
9. Grounding Blend
10. Inspiring Blend
11. Invigorating Blend
12. Joyful Blend
13. Massage Blend
14. Metabolic Blend
15. Monthly Blend
16. Protective Blend
17. Reassuring Blend
18. Renewing Blend
19. Repellent Blend
20. Respiratory Blend
21. Restful Blend
22. Skin Clearing Blend
23. Soothing Blend
24. Tension Blend
25. Uplifting Blend
26. Women's Blend

APPENDIX B

Decoding Emotions:

Tuning in to the Mind-Body Connection

Identifying the exact emotions you are experiencing at any given time can sometimes be challenging. You know that you're feeling something but may not know exactly what. Thankfully, emotions are experienced throughout the entire body, so we can look to it for clues.

Our brain's limbic system governs our emotional responses, and sends different chemical messages for the different emotions we experience. Our body has specific physical reactions to the various chemical messages, thus providing an indication as to the emotion that triggered them. For example, "stressed" is an emotional state that generally causes the release of extra adrenaline and cortisol. Those chemicals trigger physical reactions such as increased heart rate, changes in breathing, trembling, digestive upset, perspiration, and so on. If you're experiencing a combination of these symptoms, there's a good chance the emotion you're experiencing is "stressed."

While the experience of emotions can be as varied as the people having them, the following chart provides some examples of physical indicators commonly associated with the emotions provided.

Emotion	Associated Emotions	Physical Indicator	Mental or Emotional Indicator
Fear	Anxious Irritable Prideful Judgmental Scarcity Jealousy Weak Vulnerable Controlling Unsafe	Rapid or shallow breathing, increased heart rate, blood draining from face or limbs, nausea, throat contraction, clenching or tightening in chest or stomach, sweaty palms, dizziness, butterflies or fluttering in stomach, muscle weakness	Unsure, uneasy, anxious, restless, hesitant, panicked, terrified, phobias, apprehension, paranoia, worry, inability to concentrate, dread, preoccupation with future events or other people's behavior
Happiness	Contentment Joy Excitement	Warmth starting from the inside and radiating out, sometimes centered around chest, physical relaxation or increased energy, feeling of expansiveness, breathing deeper and easier, mental clarity	Pleasant thoughts and feelings, contented, satisfied, safe, elated, positive, enthusiastic, vibrant, buoyant, cheerful, serene, sense of well-being, hopeful

Emotion	Associated Emotions	Physical Indicator	Mental or Emotional Indicator
Anger	Frustration Resentment Irritation Hate Rage Blame	Tightness of muscles, pain or pressure in back, neck, and jaw, hot, adrenaline response including increased sensation in arms and hands, increased heart rate and blood pressure, shaking or trembling, sweating	Escalation of powerful, intense, or suppressed feelings, can mask fear and sadness, explosive outburst, withdrawn, silent, defensive, resentful, irritable, sarcastic or cynical
Love	Passion Fondness Forgiving Compassion	Love can be a total physical experience, generally with increased blood flow and warmth often felt primarily in the chest	Contentment, strong affection, feeling complete or filled, compassionate, general well-being, bonded, observant, selfless desires and actions
Sadness	Hurt Sorrow Loss Grief Loneliness Apathetic	Heaviness in chest, lump in throat, crying, aches and pains, lethargy and fatigue	Heavy, down, blue, apathetic, hurt, betrayed, isolated or alone, sorrowful, anguish, hopelessness or despair

Emotion	Associated Emotions	Physical Indicator	Mental or Emotional Indicator
Peaceful	Present Grounded Contentment	Relaxation in muscle tension, especially in face and upper torso, cessation or reduction of pain, warmth through body, reduced pulse, steady breathing	Calm, relaxed, patient, content, connected, serene, flexible, accepting, untroubled, purposeful
Guilt	Shame Regret	Tightening or aching sensations in the stomach and chest, or other uncomfortable sensations in the head and face as well as the lower abdomen	Fear, anger, sadness, regret, desire to run away or disappear, avoidance or denial, embarrassment, feeling like a failure or worthless

105

Emotion	Associated Emotions	Physical Indicator	Mental or Emotional Indicator
Stress	Overwhelmed Unsupported Controlled	Muscle tension in shoulders, neck, and head, overly alert or difficulty concentrating, headaches, indigestion or nausea, rapid breathing, general aches and pains, heart palpitations, changes in eating and sleep habits	Feeling pressured by people or circumstances, depleted, drained, overwhelmed, burdened, anxious, fearful, angry, sadness, hopelessness, noticeable changes in mood or behavior such as being reactive, withdrawn, indecisive, irritable, tearful, or lashing out

Though there are some general reactions and most-common occurrences that give us a fairly predictable foundation, bear in mind that it's possible to experience multiple feelings simultaneously. (For example, when we feel threatened, we often feel anger and fear at the same time.) Additionally, physical responses to very different emotions can feel quite similar. For example, the physical indicators of being terrified and exhilarated are largely the same. The brain, in context with your individual experiences and beliefs, will shape which emotion we feel and how.

APPENDIX C
Essential Oils Reference Chart

Essential Oil	Negative Emotions	Positive Properties
SINGLE OILS		
Arborvitae	Overexertion Struggle Distant from God	Grace-filled Trust Peaceful Surrender
Basil	Fatigued Depleted Dependent	Energized Renewed Rested
Bergamot	Self-judgment Insecurity Unlovable	Self-acceptance Optimism Confidence
Birch	Alienated Fear of rejection Conforming Unsupported	Supported Grounded Connected
Black Pepper	Superficial Hiding Self-deception	Honest Authentic Courageous
Cardamom	Angry Aggressive Disrespectful	Objectivity Self-control Respectful
Cassia	Fear of rejection Shy Timid	Courageous Unashamed Valuable

© Enlighten

Essential Oil	Negative Emotions	Positive Properties
Cedarwood	Separate Aloof Lonely	Connected Belonging Social
Cilantro	Controlling Worried Trapped	Unattached Cleansing Liberated
Cinnamon	Fear of rejection Sexual repression Pretense Jealousy	Attractive Healthy sexuality Intimacy Accepting
Clary Sage	Confused Limited Blocked	Clarity Intuitive Imaginative
Clove	Controlled Self-betrayal Codependency Poor boundaries	Empowered Clear boundaries Protected
Coriander	Controlled Self-betrayal Disloyalty	Integrity Inner guidance True to Self
Cypress	Rigid Perfectionistic Controlling	Trust Flow Adaptable

Essential Oil	Negative Emotions	Positive Properties
Dill	Bored Disinterested Overstimulated	Engaged Motivated Integration

Douglas Fir	Repeating mistakes
	  from the past
	Generational
	  patterns
	Negative traditions
		Wisdom
		Respectful
		Generational
		  healing
		Healthy connections

Eucalyptus	Ill Depleted Despondent Defeated	Well Responsible Liberated
Fennel	Irresponsible Loss of appetite Body neglect	Responsible Satiated In tune
Frankincense	Darkness Deception Spiritual disconnect Abandoned	Wisdom Discernment Spiritual connection
Geranium	Distrust Grief Brokenhearted	Trusting Loving Tolerant Open
Ginger	Victim Blaming Powerless	Empowered Capable Responsible

Essential Oil	Negative Emotions	Positive Properties

Grapefruit	Body judgment
	Disrespecting body
	Obsession with
	  food or dieting
		Body acceptance
		Respect for body
		Meeting physical
		  needs

Helichrysum	Traumatized Wounded Hopeless	Whole Courageous Hopeful
Jasmine	Resistant Sexual fixation Sexual trauma	Intimate Pure Healthy sexuality
Juniper Berry	Terrified Fear Nightmares	Protected Courage Dreaming
Lavender	Blocked communication Hiding Constricted Insecure	Open Relaxed Expressive
Lemon	Unfocused Fatigue Difficulty learning	Focus Energy Alert
Lemongrass	Deception Hoarding Lethargic	Clarity Simplicity Cleansing
Lime	Disinterested Despairing Resignation Apathetic	Engaged Courage Determined Grateful

Essential Oil	Negative Emotions	Positive Properties
Marjoram	Isolated Fear of rejection Cold Distrust	Connected Warm Loving
Melaleuca	Boundary violation Enmeshed Self-betrayal	Energetic boundaries Respectful connections Resilient
Melissa	Burdened Misaligned Dark	Joyful Integrity Enlightened
Myrrh	Distrusting Ungrounded Unsafe in the world	Safe Secure Trusting Nurtured
Oregano	Prideful Willful Opinionated	Humility Willingness Nonattachment
Patchouli	Obsessive Disconnected Body shame	Moderation Balanced Body contentment
Peppermint	Heavy Pessimistic Muddled	Buoyant Optimistic Clarity
Petitgrain	Inherited limitations Duty bound Unhealthy traditions	Pioneering Balanced Chain-breaking

Essential Oil	Negative Emotions	Positive Properties
Roman Chamomile	Purposeless Directionless Unsettled	Purposeful Guided Peaceful
Rose	Unlovable Wounded Disheartened	Loved Compassionate Healed
Rosemary	Confusion Ignorance Uncertain	Mental clarity Knowledgeable
Sandalwood	Prideful Materialistic Distracted	Humility Devotion Spiritual
Spearmint	Confounded Nervous Withholding voice	Clarity Confident Articulate speech
Spikenard	Ingratitude Victim mentality Resistance	Grateful Acceptance Content
Tangerine	Overburdened Overworked Stifled	Cheerful Fun Creative
Thyme	Unforgiving Intolerant Angry Resentful	Forgiving Tolerant Patient Understanding

Essential Oil	Negative Emotions	Positive Properties
Vetiver	Scattered Ungrounded Escapism Avoidant	Centered Grounded Present

White Fir	Codependent
	Destructive
	  patterns
	Generational
	  burdens
		Free
		Healthy patterns
		Generational
		  healing

Wild Orange	Scarcity Serious Rigid	Abundant Humorous Playful
Wintergreen	Controlling Self-Reliant Willful	Surrender Relying on the Divine Letting go
Ylang Ylang	Sadness Joyless Intellectual	Freedom Playful Intuitive
OIL BLENDS		
Anti-Aging Blend	Discouragement Lack of vision Spiritually cut off	Hope Transformation Trust in Divine
Cleansing Blend	Trapped Negative Cluttered	Unencumbered Refreshed Clean

113

Essential Oil	Negative Emotions	Positive Properties
Comforting Blend	Grief Loss Traumatized	Comforted Whole Serene
Detoxification Blend	Stuck Toxic habits Resistant	Revitalized Unrestricted Clear
Digestive Blend	Unenthusiastic Undernourished Overstimulated	Enthusiasm Nourished Assimilation
DNA Repairing Blend	Broken Immobilized Powerless	Repaired Balanced Rebirth Transformation
Encouraging Blend	Unmotivated Gloomy Weary	Motivated Encouraged Energized
Focus Blend	Distracted Procrastination Overactive	Focused Commitment Present
Grounding Blend	Ungrounded Disconnected Scattered	Grounded Connected Stable
Inspiring Blend	Lack of confidence Regimented Joyless	Passionate Risk-taking Spontaneous

Essential Oil	Negative Emotions	Positive Properties
Invigorating Blend	Stifled Blocked creativity Unmotivated	Invigorated Creative Motivated
Joyful Blend	Despair Discouraged Humorless	Brightness Joy Carefree
Massage Blend	Tense Stressed Rigid	Relaxed Harmonious Flexible
Metabolic Blend	Worthless Critical Strict	Worthwhile Accepting Beautiful
Monthly Blend	Invulnerable Irritable Guarded	Vulnerable Serene Receptive
Protective Blend	Attacked Unprotected Controlled	Protected Capable Independent
Reassuring Blend	Anxious Controlling Attached Afraid	Peaceful Content Still Serene
Renewing Blend	Unforgiving Critical Resentful	Forgiving Understanding Tolerant

115

Essential Oil	Negative Emotions	Positive Properties
Repellent Blend	Poor boundaries Targeted Defenseless	Boundaries Safe Self-contained
Respiratory Blend	Unloved Sadness Constricted Grief	Loved Cared for Receiving Solace
Restful Blend	Stressed Restless Disconnected	Calm Tranquil Compassionate
Skin-Clearing Blend	Self-critical Suppressed anger Inadequate	Self-acceptance Worthwhile Ample
Soothing Blend	Resistance Pained Hysterical	Strength Soothed Serene
Tension Blend	Imbalanced Burned out Tense	Equilibrium Calm Relieved
Uplifting Blend	Pessimistic Burdened Heavyhearted Hopeless	Cheerful Uplifted Hopeful
Women's Blend	Irritable Defensive Tough Overly masculine	Kind Soft Gentle Feminine

APPENDIX D
Essential Oil Emotional Usage Guide

A

Abandoned: Frankincense, Myrrh, Marjoram, Geranium

Abundance: Wild Orange, Invigorating Blend, Joyful Blend, Tangerine, Arborvitae

Abuse: Jasmine, Cinnamon, Clove, Helichrysum, White Fir, Cardamom, Douglas Fir

Accepted/Acceptance: Rose, Bergamot, Jasmine, Spikenard

Accountability: (see Responsibility)

Adaptable: Women's Blend

Adjustment, difficulty with: Rosemary, Detoxification Blend

Afraid: (see Fear/Fearful)

Agitated: Restful Blend, (see also Irritated)

Alienated: Birch, Cedarwood, Myrrh, Arborvitae

Aloof: Marjoram, Grounding Blend, Jasmine, Detoxification Blend

Anger: Cardamom, Thyme, Renewing Blend, Geranium, Ylang Ylang, Skin-Clearing Blend, Women's Blend

Anguish: Helichrysum, Anti-Aging Blend, Melissa, Skin-Clearing Blend

Annoyed: Rose, Cardamom

Anxious: Comforting Blend, Basil, Respiratory Blend, Tension Blend, Restful Blend

Apathy/Apathetic: Lemongrass, Vetiver, Lime, Detoxification Blend

Appearance, negative image of: (see Body, hate for)

Appetite, loss of: Digestive Blend, Fennel

Appreciative: (see Gratitude)

Apprehensive: Cassia, Cinnamon, Melissa

Approved of: Rose, Bergamot

Argumentative: Lavender, Cardamom

Arrogant: Women's Blend, Monthly Blend, Oregano

Ashamed: (see Shame)

Assertive: Clove, Encouraging Blend, Black Pepper

Attacked: Protective Blend, Repellent Blend, Birch

Attached, overly: Oregano, Sandalwood, Detoxification Blend, Reassuring Blend

Attentive: Lemon, Focus Blend

Authentic: Wild Orange, Cassia, Spearmint

Avoidance: Soothing Blend, Vetiver, Helichrysum, Grounding Blend, Juniper Berry, Jasmine

B

Balanced: Petitgrain

Barriers, emotional: Marjoram, Monthly Blend, Restful Blend, Rose

Beaten down: Protective Blend, Uplifting Blend, Encouraging Blend

Believing: (see Faith)

Belittled: Bergamot, Metabolic Blend

Bereaved: (see Grief)

Betrayed: Geranium, Rose, Ylang Ylang

Bitterness: Renewing Blend, Thyme

Blaming others: Cardamom, Renewing Blend, Skin-Clearing Blend, Vetiver, Ginger

Blaming self: Bergamot, Clove, Ginger, Renewing Blend

Blindness, spiritual: Anti-Aging Blend, Clary Sage, Lemongrass, Frankincense

Blocked, emotionally: Cypress, Thyme, Oregano

Body shame: Patchouli, Jasmine, Grapefruit, Metabolic Blend

Body tension: Tension Blend, Massage Blend, Patchouli

Body, hate for: Grapefruit, Metabolic Blend, Cinnamon, Skin-Clearing Blend

Body, judgment of: Grapefruit, Metabolic Blend, Patchouli, Cinnamon, Skin-Clearing Blend

Bonding: Geranium, Marjoram, Douglas Fir, Myrrh, Cedarwood

Bored: Dill

Boundaries, poor: Protective Blend, Melaleuca, Clove, Repellent Blend, Oregano, Cardamom

Bragging: (see Pride)

Brave: (see Courage)

Breath, constricted: Respiratory Blend, Massage Blend, Peppermint, White Fir, Arborvitae

Burdened: Anti-Aging Blend, White Fir, Wintergreen, Arborvitae, Tangerine, Restful Blend, DNA Repairing Blend, Cilantro, Renewing Blend, Uplifting Blend, Inspiring Blend, Encouraging Blend, Douglas Fir, Comforting Blend

Burned out: Basil, Tension Blend, Uplifting Blend, Encouraging Blend, Arborvitae, Respiratory Blend

C

Calm: Restful Blend, Lavender, Reassuring Blend, Lemon, Patchouli, Roman Chamomile, Sandalwood, Massage Blend, Cardamom, Arborvitae, Women's Blend, Tension Blend, Focus Blend

Careless: (see Apathy/Apathetic)

Centered: Vetiver, Roman Chamomile, Restful Blend, Clove, Cardamom

Chain-breaking: Petitgrain

Change, resistance to: Cilantro

Chaotic: Lemon, Vetiver, Restful Blend, Cardamom

Cheated: (see Betrayed)

Cheerful: Tangerine, Uplifting Blend, Lime, Wild Orange, Invigorating Blend, Joyful Blend, Arborvitae

Childish: Invigorating Blend

Clarity, mental: Lemon, Rosemary, Cardamom, Spearmint

Clarity, spiritual: Clary Sage, Frankincense, Sandalwood, Arborvitae, Lemongrass

Clean: Cleansing Blend, Lemongrass, Bergamot, Frankincense, Detoxification Blend, Jasmine, Cilantro

Clear-minded: Lemon, Cardamom

Clingy: Eucalyptus, Ylang Ylang

Closed, emotionally: Respiratory Blend, Ylang Ylang, Monthly Blend, Rose, Geranium, Jasmine, Detoxification Blend

Closed-minded: (see Narrow-minded)

Codependent: Melaleuca, Clove, Protective Blend, Cleansing Blend, Oregano, Ginger, Jasmine

Cold: (see Aloof)

Comforted: Comforting Blend, Uplifting Blend, Rose, Roman Chamomile, Anti-Aging Blend, Massage Blend, Joyful Blend, Soothing Blend, Tension Blend

Committed: Ginger, Coriander, Grounding Blend

Communication, blocked: Lavender, Spearmint, Monthly Blend

Compassion: Rose, Restful Blend, Geranium

Competitive: Women's Blend, Helichrysum, Arborvitae

Complaining: Joyful Blend, Ylang Ylang

Composed: Patchouli, Cardamom

Compulsive: Sandalwood, Black Pepper, Vetiver, Jasmine, Detoxification Blend

Conceited: Women's Blend, Oregano, Monthly Blend

Condemning: (see Judgmental)

Confidence: Bergamot, Cassia, Encouraging Blend, Spearmint, Roman Chamomile, Lavender, Invigorating Blend

Conforming: Coriander, Clove, Ginger, Cassia

Confused/Confusion: Clary Sage, Lemon, Peppermint, Rosemary

Connected, emotionally: Marjoram, Vetiver, Cedarwood, Geranium, Restful Blend

Connected, mentally: Rosemary, Cardamom, Lemon

Connected, physically: Patchouli, Grounding Blend, Restful Blend

Connected, spiritually: Frankincense, Melissa, Roman Chamomile, Sandalwood

Consciousness, higher: Sandalwood, Anti-Aging Blend, Joyful Blend, Helichrysum, Frankincense

Consoled: (See Comforted)

Constricted: Lavender, Cypress, Arborvitae, Detoxification Blend

Content: Tangerine, Arborvitae, Reassuring Blend, Comforting Blend, Spikenard, Restful Blend

Contentious: Cardamom, Thyme

Controlled: Protective Blend, Clove, Coriander, Cilantro

Controlling: Cinnamon, Wintergreen, Cypress, Sandalwood, Metabolic Blend, Cilantro, Cardamom, Arborvitae, Reassuring Blend

Courage: Helichrysum, Birch, Cassia, Clove, Ginger, Repellent Blend, Uplifting Blend, Encouraging Blend

Cowardly: (see Courage)

Cranky: Women's Blend, Monthly Blend, Cardamom

Creative: Wild Orange, Tangerine, Invigorating Blend, Clary Sage, Inspiring Blend

Creativity, blocked or stifled: Invigorating Blend, Tangerine, Wild Orange, Clary Sage, Inspiring Blend

Crisis: Lavender, Basil, Peppermint, Geranium, Vetiver

Critical: Bergamot, Metabolic Blend, Thyme, Skin-Clearing Blend, Cardamom, Renewing Blend

Cursed: Melissa

Cynical: Renewing Blend, Wild Orange, Tangerine, Skin-Clearing Blend

D

Dark, fear of: Juniper Berry

Dark, in the: Anti-Aging Blend, Melissa, Clary Sage, Frankincense, Joyful Blend

Darkness: Lemongrass, Frankincense, Melaleuca, Anti-Aging Blend

Death wish: (see Loss of will to live)

Death, acceptance of: Roman Chamomile, Frankincense

Deceived: Clary Sage, Frankincense

Decisive: Lemon, Clove

Defeated: Clove, Invigorating Blend, Jasmine, Eucalyptus, Ginger, Fennel, Arborvitae, Uplifting Blend

Defenseless: Repellent Blend, Protective Blend

Defensive: Oregano, Cardamom, Women's Blend, Monthly Blend, Ylang Ylang, Geranium

Defiant: Oregano, Cardamom, Women's Blend, Ylang Ylang

Defiled: Cleansing Blend, Thyme

Degraded: Bergamot, Clove

Denial: (see Avoidance)

Dependent: Melaleuca, Clove, Ginger, Jasmine

Depleted: Basil, Peppermint, Arborvitae, Uplifting Blend, Encouraging Blend, Jasmine

Despair: Joyful Blend, Peppermint, Melissa, Encouraging Blend

Desire, lack of: Encouraging Blend, Grounding Blend, Fennel, Black Pepper, Jasmine, Invigorating Blend, Lemongrass, Detoxification Blend

Despair: Joyful Blend, Melissa, Uplifting Blend, Encouraging Blend, Bergamot, Respiratory Blend, Eucalyptus, Lemongrass, DNA Repairing Blend

Despondent: Lemongrass, Melissa, Encouraging Blend, Detoxification Blend, Eucalyptus, Grounding Blend, Invigorating Blend

Dieting, obsession with: Bergamot, Detoxification Blend, Frankincense, Peppermint, Vetiver, White Fir

Discerning/Discernment: Clary Sage, Frankincense, Lemongrass

Disconnected from body: Patchouli, Grounding Blend, Focus Blend, Jasmine, Restful Blend

Disconnection, spiritual: Frankincense, Sandalwood, Clary Sage

Discontent: Wild Orange, Restful Blend, Cardamom, Skin-Clearing Blend

Discouraged: Lime, Melissa, Joyful Blend, Wild Orange, Encouraging Blend, Roman Chamomile, Anti-Aging Blend, DNA Repairing Blend

Disharmony: Grounding Blend, Restful Blend, Cardamom, Arborvitae

Disheartened: Rose, Geranium

Dishonest: Black Pepper, Vetiver, Cassia, Lavender, Geranium, Monthly Blend

Disinterested: Dill

Disengaged: Dill

Distant: Marjoram, Jasmine, Cedarwood, Arborvitae, Restful Blend

Distracted: Focus Blend

Distraught: Anti-Aging Blend, Lemongrass

Distrusting: Geranium, Marjoram, Myrrh, Arborvitae, Jasmine, Renewing Blend

Divided/Double minded: Grounding Blend, Vetiver, Lemon

Dominated: Clove, Protective Blend, Repellent Blend, Ginger

Doubtful: Sandalwood, DNA Repairing Blend

Drained: Basil, Melaleuca, Tension Blend, Massage Blend, Arborvitae, Uplifting Blend, Encouraging Blend

Dread: Fennel, Monthly Blend

Drudgery: Inspiring Blend, Roman Chamomile, Coriander, Invigorating Blend, Fennel

Dull: Inspiring Blend, Invigorating Blend, Wild Orange, Roman Chamomile, Detoxification Blend

Dumb, feeling: Lemon, Peppermint, Rosemary

Duty bound: Petitgrain

E

Egotistical: Women's Blend, Oregano, Arborvitae, Rose

Elevated: Joyful Blend, Lime, Melissa

Embarrassed: Cassia, Jasmine

Empathy: Monthly Blend, Geranium, Rose

Empowered: Arborvitae, Ginger, Clove

Emptiness: Vetiver, Sandalwood, Arborvitae

Energized: Basil, Encouraging Blend, Respiratory Blend, Arborvitae

Energy, lack of: Lemon, Encouraging Blend, Peppermint, Wild Orange, Arborvitae, Joyful Blend, Invigorating Blend

Engaged: Dill

Enlightened: Melissa, Frankincense, Sandalwood

Entangled: Melaleuca, Clove, Protective Blend, Oregano

Enthusiasm: Melissa, Encouraging Blend, Respiratory Blend

Envy: (See Jealousy)

Escapism: Vetiver, Focus Blend, Patchouli, Grounding Blend, Jasmine

Estranged: (see Separated)

Exasperated: Basil, Respiratory Blend, Lavender

Excessive: Grounding Blend, Sandalwood, Jasmine

Exhausted: Basil, Restful Blend

F

Façade, emotional: Black Pepper, Vetiver, Soothing Blend, Helichrysum

Failure, feeling like: Bergamot, Roman Chamomile

Faith: Anti-Aging Blend, Sandalwood, Arborvitae, Uplifting Blend

Faithless: Anti-Aging Blend, Sandalwood, Arborvitae

Father, issues with: Frankincense

Fatigue, mental: Lemon, Respiratory Blend, Rosemary

Fatigued: Restful Blend, Basil, Respiratory Blend, Tension Blend, Encouraging Blend

Fear/Fearful: Juniper Berry, Cassia, Cinnamon, Jasmine, Birch, Cypress, Lavender, Myrrh, Arborvitae, Reassuring Blend, Inspiring Blend, Comforting Blend

Fearless: Juniper Berry, Clove, Inspiring Blend

Firm: Clove, Birch

Flexibility: Cypress, Massage Blend, Arborvitae, Wild Orange

Flighty: Grounding Blend

Focus, inability to: Lemon, Focus Blend, Peppermint

Focused: Lemon, Focus Blend, Rosemary, Grounding Blend, Cardamom, Roman Chamomile, Spearmint

Food, preoccupation with: Grapefruit, Metabolic Blend, Detoxification Blend

Foolish, feeling: Cassia

Forgetful: Lemon, Peppermint

Forgiveness: Thyme, Renewing Blend, Geranium

Fragmented: Vetiver, Cardamom, Grounding Blend

Frantic: (see Hurried)

Friendless: Marjoram, Cedarwood

Frustrated: Geranium, Cardamom, Roman Chamomile

Fulfilled: Roman Chamomile, Jasmine, Reassuring Blend

G

Generational issues: White Fir, Douglas Fir, DNA Repairing Blend, Birch, Jasmine

Gentle: Geranium, Ylang Ylang, Anti-Aging Blend

Giving up: Helichrysum, Soothing Blend, Uplifting Blend, Detoxification Blend

Gratitude/Grateful: Wild Orange, Helichrysum, Tension Blend, Anti-Aging Blend, Douglas Fir, Spikenard

Greed: Wild Orange, Spikenard

Grief: Respiratory Blend, Soothing Blend, Geranium, Lime, Comforting Blend

Grouchy: Cardamom, Women's Blend, Thyme

Grounded: Grounding Blend, Birch, Patchouli, Vetiver, Focus Blend, Arborvitae, Anti-Aging Blend

Guarded: Monthly Blend, Jasmine

Guilt: Bergamot, Lemon, Peppermint, Skin-Clearing Blend

H

Harassed: Protective Blend, Repellent Blend

Hardened: Rose, Geranium, Ylang Ylang, Jasmine, Tangerine

Hardhearted: Rose, Geranium, Thyme

Harsh: Cardamom, Marjoram, Geranium

Hate/Hatred: Thyme, Cardamom

Haughty: (see Egotistical)

Haunted: Frankincense, Protective Blend, Melissa

Headstrong: Cardamom, Oregano, Wild Orange,
   Women's Blend, Lime

Healed: Helichrysum, Geranium, Eucalyptus, Jasmine,
   Comforting Blend

Heartbroken: Geranium, Rose

Heartless: Rose, Geranium, Cardamom

Heavyhearted: Lime, Joyful Blend, Uplifting Blend, Geranium

Helpless/Helplessness: Clove, Ginger, Protective Blend,
   Uplifting Blend

Hereditary issues: (see Generational Issues)

Hesitant: (see Indecisive)

Hiding: Cassia, Black Pepper

High-strung: Massage Blend

Hoarding: Lemongrass, Myrrh, Cleansing Blend, Detoxification
   Blend, Thyme, Wild Orange

Holding back: Cassia, Spearmint, Lavender, Jasmine

Holding onto the past: Thyme, Lemongrass, Cleansing Blend,
   Detoxification Blend, Wintergreen

Honest: Black Pepper, Geranium, Lavender

Hopeless: Melissa, Clary Sage, Anti-Aging Blend, Uplifting Blend

Humiliated: Cassia

Humor, sense of: Wild Orange, Joyful Blend

Hurried: Massage Blend, Tension Blend, Restful Blend

Hurtful to others: Cardamom, Women's Blend, Rose

Hypocritical: Clary Sage, Frankincense
Hysterical: Grounding Blend, Soothing Blend

I

Illness, attached to: Eucalyptus
Imbalanced, emotionally: Restful Blend, Invigorating Blend
Immature, emotionally: Geranium, Fennel
Immobilized: Cypress, Thyme, Uplifting Blend
Immoral: Frankincense, Detoxification Blend, Cleansing Blend,
    Jasmine, Vetiver
Impatient/Impatience: (see Anxious)
Impoverished: Wild Orange
Imprisoned: Eucalyptus, Lavender, Detoxification Blend
Inadequate: Bergamot, Metabolic Blend, Skin-Clearing Blend
Incapable: Bergamot
Inconsiderate of others: Cardamom, Cinnamon
Inconsistent: Grounding Blend, Coriander Indecisive: Lemon,
    Peppermint
Indifferent: (see Apathy/Apathetic)
Inferior: Bergamot.
Inflexible: Cypress, Massage Blend, Arborvitae, Wild Orange
Ingratitude: Spikenard
Innocent: Ylang Ylang, Geranium, Jasmine
Insecure: Cassia, Bergamot
Insignificant: Roman Chamomile
Inspired: Inspiring Blend, Uplifting Blend, Encouraging Blend,
    Joyful Blend
Instability: Grounding Blend, Arborvitae
Intimidated: Clove, Repellent Blend, Ginger
Intolerant: Geranium, Cardamom, Rose, Skin-Clearing Blend,
    Renewing Blend
Introvert: Marjoram, Cedarwood
Invigorated: Peppermint, Lemon, Invigorating Blend

© Enlighten

Invulnerable: Monthly Blend, Marjoram
Irresponsible: Fennel, Ginger, Grounding Blend
Irritable/Irritated: Women's Blend, Monthly Blend, Cardamom
Isolated: Cedarwood, Arborvitae, Marjoram, Restful Blend

J

Jealousy: Cinnamon
Joy, lack of: Joyful Blend, Arborvitae, Lemon, Ylang Ylang, Uplifting Blend, Inspiring Blend
Joyful: Lemon, Lime, Wild Orange, Tangerine, Peppermint, Ylang Ylang, Invigorating Blend, Joyful Blend, Arborvitae, Uplifting Blend
Judged: Birch, Clove, Ginger, Cassia
Judgmental: Cardamom, Women's Blend, Renewing Blend, Restful Blend, Geranium, Rose, Ylang Ylang, Black Pepper

K

Kindness: Anti-Aging Blend, Geranium
Know-it-all: Oregano, Women's Blend, Rosemary, Wintergreen, Sandalwood

L

Learning Issues: Lemon, Rosemary, Digestive Blend
Left out: Cedarwood, Marjoram, Myrrh
Lethargy: Lemongrass, Invigorating Blend, Encouraging Blend
Liberated: Detoxification Blend, Cleansing Blend, Lavender, Melissa, Arborvitae, Renewing Blend
Lighthearted: (see Joyful)
Limited thinking: Oregano, Rosemary, Coriander, Digestive Blend
Loneliness: Marjoram, Cedarwood, Frankincense, Myrrh
Loss: Geranium, Ylang Ylang, Comforting Blend
Lost/Purposeless: Roman Chamomile, Frankincense

Loss of will to live: Invigorating Blend, Melissa, Anti-Aging Blend,
   Frankincense, Lime
Love, unconditional: Rose, Geranium
Loved: Frankincense, Rose, Respiratory Blend
Low self-esteem/Self-worth: Bergamot, Metabolic Blend, Jasmine,
   Skin-Clearing Blend
Loyal: Coriander, Jasmine
Lustful: Cinnamon, Jasmine

M

Mad: (see Anger)
Manipulated: Clove, Protective Blend
Manipulative: Cinnamon, Monthly Blend
Masculine, overly: Women's Blend, Monthly Blend
Masking, emotional: Black Pepper
Materialistic: Sandalwood, Oregano, Cilantro, Detoxification Blend
Maternal connection, disrupted: Myrrh, Monthly Blend,
   Women's Blend
Mature, emotionally: Geranium, Fennel
Mean: Geranium, Ylang Ylang, Cardamom, Women's Blend,
   Monthly Blend
Melancholy: (see Sadness, Despair)
Menopause, dread of: Monthly Blend, Jasmine, Grapefruit
Menstruation, dread of: Monthly Blend, Jasmine, Grapefruit
Moody/Unstable moods: Joyful Blend
Motivated: Encouraging Blend, Invigorating Blend,
   Black Pepper, Dill
Moving forward: (see Stagnant)

N

Narrow-minded: Rosemary, Oregano, Wild Orange, Lemon

Need for approval: Bergamot

Negative Habits: Bergamot, Detoxification Blend, Frankincense, Jasmine, Peppermint, Vetiver, White Fir, Douglas Fir

Neglected: Monthly Blend, Cedarwood, Myrrh, Marjoram

Nervousness: Spearmint, Basil, Wild Orange, Tension Blend, Restful Blend

Nightmares: Juniper Berry

Not enough: (see Scarcity)

O

Obsessed: Patchouli, Jasmine, Grounding Blend, Detoxification Blend

Obsessive-compulsive: Bergamot, Sandalwood, Cleansing Blend, Jasmine, Restful Blend

Offended: Cardamom, Geranium, Renewing Blend

Open-minded: Clary Sage, Wild Orange, Massage Blend

Opinionated: Oregano

Oppressed: Clove, Protective Blend, White Fir

Optimism: Melissa, Invigorating Blend, Tangerine, Bergamot

Out of control: Cardamom, Grounding Blend, Jasmine

Overanalyzing: Wild Orange, Restful Blend, Ylang Ylang

Overly empathetic: (see Boundaries, poor)

Overstimulation: Digestive Blend, Grounding Blend, Dill

Overthinking: Sandalwood, Restful Blend, Myrrh, Ylang Ylang, Wild Orange

Overwhelmed: Basil, Restful Blend, Massage Blend, Tension Blend, Digestive Blend, Tangerine

Overworked: Tangerine, Wild Orange, Ylang Ylang, Tension Blend, Arborvitae, Inspiring Blend, Encouraging Blend

P

Pain, emotional: Helichrysum, Soothing Blend, Geranium, Skin-Clearing Blend, Comforting Blend

Pain, resistance to: Soothing Blend, Helichrysum

Panic: Grounding Blend, Soothing Blend

Passionate: Jasmine, Inspiring Blend, Detoxification Blend

Patience: Cardamom, Grounding Blend, Anti-Aging Blend, Uplifting Blend

Peaceful: Reassuring Blend, Roman Chamomile, Restful Blend, Joyful Blend, Cardamom, Arborvitae, Comforting Blend

Peer pressure: Ginger, Clove, Protective Blend

Perfectionism: Cypress, Arborvitae, Cardamom

Persecuted: Protective Blend

Perseverance: Helichrysum, Grounding Blend, Uplifting Blend, Encouraging Blend

Pessimistic: Wild Orange, Peppermint, Uplifting Blend

Pioneering: Petitgrain

Playful: Ylang Ylang, Inspiring Blend, Wild Orange, Tangerine

Poor, financially: Wild Orange

Possessive: Sandalwood, Oregano, Wintergreen, Reassuring Blend

Powerless to heal: Arborvitae, Eucalyptus

Powerless: Clove, Ginger, Arborvitae, Jasmine

Pretense: Black Pepper, Cinnamon

Pride: Oregano, Women's Blend, Sandalwood, Wintergreen

Procrastination: Focus Blend

Protected: Protective Blend, Clove, Repellent Blend, Frankincense, Juniper Berry, Reassuring Blend

Punishing, self: Bergamot, Jasmine, Metabolic Blend

Pure: Jasmine, Cleansing Blend, Lemongrass

Purposeful: Roman Chamomile, Ginger

Purposeless: Roman Chamomile

Q

Quarrelsome: Women's Blend, Oregano, Cardamom
Quick-tempered: Cardamom, Geranium, Monthly Blend
Quitting: Helichrysum, Encouraging blend, Arborvitae,
Uplifting Blend

R

Rage: Cardamom, Thyme
Rational: Lemon, Cardamom
Reclusive: Marjoram, Cedarwood
Reinforced: Protective Blend, Birch, Cedarwood, Arborvitae
Rejection, fear of: Lavender, Cinnamon, Lime
Relationships, codependent: Melaleuca, Clove, Protective Blend,
Ginger, Jasmine
Relationships, parasitic: Melaleuca, Protective Blend, Oregano,
Jasmine, Detoxification Blend
Relaxed: Tension Blend, Restful Blend, Arborvitae, Lavender,
Roman Chamomile, Reassuring Blend
Relieved: Helichrysum, Tension Blend, Arborvitae, Peppermint,
Uplifting Blend
Renewed: Basil, Peppermint, Arborvitae, Restful Blend,
Encouraging Blend
Repressed: Lavender, Vetiver, Black Pepper, Jasmine
Resentment: Geranium, Thyme, Cardamom, Renewing Blend
Resignation: Lime, Melissa, Detoxification Blend, Uplifting Blend,
Encouraging Blend
Resistance: Arborvitae, Vetiver, Soothing Blend, Digestive Blend,
Spikenard
Resolute: Birch
Responsibility: Ginger, Fennel, Cardamom, Grounding Blend
Revitalized: Basil, Respiratory Blend, Lime, Detoxification Blend

Rigid: Cypress, Arborvitae, Oregano, Wild Orange, Tangerine, Inspiring Blend

Rushed: (see Hurried)

S

Sadness: Respiratory Blend, Ylang Ylang, Geranium, Peppermint, Massage Blend, Uplifting Blend, Comforting Blend

Scarcity: Wild Orange, Arborvitae

Scattered: Vetiver, Grounding Blend, Focus Blend

Secure: (see Protected)

Self, weak sense of: Lemon, Bergamot, Vetiver, Ginger, Jasmine, Grounding Blend, Fennel

Self-acceptance: Bergamot, Grapefruit, Metabolic Blend, Jasmine, Lemon

Self-assured: (see Confidence)

Self-betrayal: Coriander

Self-criticism: Metabolic Blend, Bergamot

Self-doubt: (see Confidence)

Self-expression: Lavender, Spearmint, Invigorating Blend, Jasmine, Inspiring Blend

Self-judgment: Bergamot, Metabolic Blend

Self-love: (see Self-Acceptance)

Self-sabotage: Metabolic Blend

Selfish: Spikenard

Sensitive, overly: Repellent Blend, Protective Blend, Clove, Ginger

Separated: Myrrh, Frankincense, Cedarwood, Arborvitae, Reassuring Blend

Serious, overly: Tangerine, Invigorating Blend, Joyful Blend, Wild Orange, Inspiring Blend, Restful Blend

Sexual identity, acceptance of: Cinnamon, Jasmine

Sexual repression: Jasmine, Cinnamon

Sexually imbalanced: Jasmine, Cinnamon, Women's Blend

Shame, body: Patchouli, Grapefruit, Metabolic Blend, Jasmine

133

Shame: Bergamot, Frankincense

Shock: Lavender, Basil, Peppermint, Wintergreen

Shy: Cassia, Spearmint, Cinnamon, Ginger

Sickly: Eucalyptus, Patchouli

Soothed: (See Comforted)

Soul, dark night of: Anti-Aging Blend, Melissa, Frankincense, Helichrysum

Speaking, fear of: Spearmint, Lavender, Jasmine

Spontaneity: Wild Orange, Invigorating Blend, Tangerine, Inspiring Blend

Stable: Grounding Blend

Stagnant: (see Stuck)

Stern: Joyful Blend, Wild Orange, Invigorating Blend, Women's Blend

Stiffness (body or mind): Massage Blend, Cypress

Stillness: Reassuring Blend, Sandalwood, Arborvitae

Strength: Birch, Protective Blend, Wintergreen, Arborvitae, Uplifting Blend

Stressed: Restful Blend, Massage Blend, Ylang Ylang, Tension Blend, Basil, Comforting Blend

Stubborn: Wintergreen, Oregano, Arborvitae

Stuck: Cypress, Lemongrass, Thyme, Detoxification Blend, Encouraging Blend, Birch, Fennel, DNA Repairing Blend

Superficial: Black Pepper

Supported: Birch, Cedarwood, Arborvitae

Surrender: Wintergreen, Arborvitae, Sandalwood, Reassuring Blend

T

Teachable: Wintergreen, Oregano, Rosemary

Tenderhearted: Geranium, Rose, Ylang Ylang

Tense: Massage Blend, Tension Blend, Cypress, Arborvitae, Women's Blend, Comforting Blend

Terror/Terrified: Juniper Berry

Thankful: (see Gratitude)

Timid: (see Shy)

Tired: Basil, Restful Blend, Invigorating Blend, Detoxification Blend

Tolerant: Thyme, Cardamom, Geranium, Renewing Blend

Toxic energy: Lemongrass, Melaleuca, Cardamom, Detoxification Blend, Cleansing Blend

Toxicity: Melaleuca, Detoxification Blend, Cleansing Blend, Lemongrass, DNA Repairing Blend, Cilantro

Transitioning, difficulty with: Rosemary, Detoxification Blend, DNA Repairing Blend

Trapped: Lavender, Thyme, Cleansing Blend, Detoxification Blend, Black Pepper, Cilantro, Arborvitae, Jasmine

Trauma, Emotional: Geranium, Clove, Helichrysum, Jasmine, Ylang Ylang, Comforting Blend

Trust: Geranium, Marjoram, Myrrh, Arborvitae, Renewing Blend, Reassuring Blend, Rosemary, Jasmine, Anti-Aging Blend

U

Ugly, feeling: Metabolic Blend, Grapefruit, Skin-Clearing Blend

Undecided: (see Indecisive)

Unforgiving: Thyme, Rose, Geranium, Cardamom

Unfulfilled: Jasmine, Roman Chamomile, Inspiring Blend

Ungrateful: (see Gratitude)

Ungrounded: Grounding Blend, Focus Blend, Vetiver, Patchouli, Myrrh, Birch, Arborvitae

Unhealthy traditions: Petitgrain

Unheard: Lavender

Unlovable: Bergamot, Respiratory Blend, Jasmine

Unloving: Geranium, Rose, Cardamom, Thyme, Renewing Blend

Unprotected: Protective Blend, Repellent Blend

Unsafe in the world: Myrrh, Protective Blend, Jasmine, Reassuring Blend

Unseen: Lavender, Cassia, Spearmint

Unsettled: Comforting Blend, Restful Blend, Roman Chamomile, Cardamom

Unsupported: Birch, Cedarwood, Arborvitae

Unteachable: Rosemary, Women's Blend, Oregano

Unyielding: (see Stubborn)

Upheld: (see Supported)

V

Victim: Clove, Ginger, Jasmine, Skin-Clearing Blend, Renewing Blend, Spikenard

Violated: Protective Blend, Ginger, Clove, Jasmine, Renewing Blend

Violent: Cardamom, Frankincense

Virtuous: Jasmine, Cinnamon, Frankincense

Vision, spiritual: Clary Sage

Vulnerable: Monthly Blend, Jasmine, Protective Blend, Arborvitae, Repellent Blend, Reassuring Blend

W

Weak-willed: Birch, Melaleuca, Ginger, Clove, Wintergreen

Weary: Restful Blend, Basil, Encouraging Blend, Invigorating Blend

Whole-minded: Rosemary

Willful, excessively: Oregano, Wintergreen, Cardamom, Arborvitae

Wisdom: Douglas Fir

Withdrawn: (see Isolated)

Workaholic: Wild Orange, Ylang Ylang, Tangerine, Arborvitae, Invigorating Blend

Worried: Wild Orange, Tangerine, Sandalwood, Cilantro

Worthless, feeling: Cassia, Bergamot, Metabolic Blend

Wounded: Helichrysum, Comforting Blend, Jasmine

APPENDIX E
Bonus Oil Blend Recipes

These are four of our favorite emotional blends, which we have created and used over the years. We want to share these recipes with you so you can enjoy them as well. To blend these oils, use a 5 ml. glass bottle. To mix a larger quantity of oil, either multiply the recipe by two or three, or dilute by adding fractionated coconut oil or another carrier oil into your blend. To create each blend, simply add the number of drops listed below in the order they are listed and mix. The blends are organized from the most simple to the most complex to create.

Appreciation Blend

50 drops Wild Orange
50 drops Frankincense

This simple blend assists feelings of gratitude and appreciation. Appreciation Blend is fantastic for diffusing in the office or home environment. It is helpful in setting a relaxed or calm atmosphere.

Rejuvenate Blend

35 drops Lemon
35 drops Cypress
35 drops Basil

Rejuvenate Blend is helpful for physical and mental fatigue and depletion. It helps to renew the mind and revive one's emotional life when a person has become mentally exhausted and/or when overuse of one's mind has subdued one's feelings. In this way, Rejuvenate Blend can assist the integration of heart and mind.

Centered Blend

10 drops Helichrysum
20 drops Lemon
20 drops Wild Orange
40 drops Vetiver

Centered Blend is very helpful for sensitive individuals who are highly affected by emotions in their environment. These individuals find it difficult to be in crowds or socialize. They have a tendency to feel nervous or burned out from external stimuli. Centered Blend helps these individuals to rediscover and deeply connect with their own center. It encourages feelings of centeredness and peace.

Note: This blend is also a personal favorite to use with children after school or before bedtime. It can soothe external influences and help a child to find their ground again.

Forgiven Blend

1   drop Rose
3   drops Tangerine
2   drops Ylang Ylang
51 drops Lime
10 drops Geranium
3   drops Marjoram
5   drops Ylang Ylang (yes, a second time)
1   drop Vetiver
1   toothpick of Jasmine (dip the end of the toothpick into
     your bottle of Jasmine, then stir into your blend)
1   drop Sandalwood

This is one of our absolute favorite blends. Forgiven Blend was formulated to dramatically assist individuals in opening their heart to feel the unconditional love of the Divine. It is soothing for periods of intense grief, sadness or loss. It also assists individuals who desire to reconnect to their own heart. This blend reminds individuals of their innocent and compassionate nature. It encourages forgiveness, especially forgiveness of one's self. It teaches that while we may hold on to or remember our glaring faults, issues and weaknesses, the source of Divine love has already forgiven us.

APPENDIX F

How to Host a Class on Emotions & Essential Oils

General Guidelines

In this appendix, we suggest classes you may host on *Emotions & Essential Oils*. Note that the following class suggestions utilize this book's companion audio lecture, a CD entitled *Emotions & Essential Oils: The Five Stages of Healing*. This audio lecture is available at www.enlightenhealing.com. We also have newly developed classes with additional support products available on our website.

Keep in mind that the individual hosting these classes should ideally have an ample amount of experience with emotional healing themselves. To direct a class and assist others in keeping their comments appropriate, it is best to have some experience in this area. This does not mean you have to be an emotional health expert, just that you have some experience with the subject.

Note: Following any class, it is a good idea to encourage the group to practice the material presented by using the essential oils and freewriting regularly. If your group is unfamiliar with freewriting, you may want to briefly explain the process or simply play the bonus track (track 10) from the audio lecture mentioned above for the group.

CLASS OPTION A: INTRODUCTORY CLASS

Class Option A introduces the concept of emotional healing with essential oils—that it's possible! This class is ideal for those who are new or unfamiliar with the concept.

Steps:

1) Introduce this book, *Emotions & Essential Oils,* to the class. Explore its basic premise: that in addition to their physical properties, essential oils assist in emotional healing as well.

Consider summarizing concepts from the audio lecture *Emotions & Essential Oils: The Five Stages of Healing* or from this book to share with the class. If you are uncomfortable sharing in front of a group, or do not feel you understand the material adequately enough to share with others, consider sharing track 2 or 3 from the audio lecture and discussing it with the group. Or you may want to read "Healing Emotions with Essential Oils" from Section I of this book (pages 7-10). If you share from the audio lecture or this book, take a few minutes to discuss what you share with the group and answer any questions.

2) Share appropriate personal experiences and stories you have encountered about the emotional healing properties of oils. Keep this section brief and to the point. If you do not have any stories or personal experiences to share with the group, consider reading "Kallie's Story" from Section I of this book.

Note: Do not try to convince your audience that oils work on this level. Each person must come to an understanding of oils' subtle healing abilities on their own. While offering a small amount of scientific background or evidence on the subject may be helpful for your audience, trying to convince or persuade individuals will never work. Allow people space and room to grow in their own way and in their own timing. Do not give them more information than they are ready for, or more than they can handle at one

141

© Enlighten

time. You must be sensitive to the needs and maturity level of the specific group you are working with. Most individuals need some time (months to years) to work with essential oils on the physical level before they are ready or even willing to explore the subtle nature of the oils.

3) Choose either activity one or two from the audio lecture, *Emotions & Essential Oils: The Five Stages of Healing* to do with the group. You may either summarize these activities in your own words, or play the tracks from the audio CD for the group.

ACTIVITY ONE
- Track 4 Stage Two: Healing the Heart (this track establishes a foundation for the first activity)
- Track 5 Activity One
- Track 6 Invitation & Clarifications for Activity One

ACTIVITY TWO
- Track 7 Activity Two
- Track 8 Invitation & Clarifications for Activity Two

4) Invite the class to experiment with the emotional properties of essential oils. Challenge them to regularly use the oil(s) they chose from the activity.

5) Wrap up the class. If you feel comfortable answering people's questions, take a few moments to do so.

CLASS OPTION B: INTERMEDIATE CLASS

Class Option B highlights one essential oil, exploring it in detail. The purpose of this class is to allow the presenter an opportunity to study an essential oil in depth and practice sharing in front of a group. This class can also provide a deeper understanding of the oils for those attending. The aim of the class is to explore the physical and the emotional properties of an essential oil. Keep in mind the preparation for such a class may be extensive.

Steps:

1) Just as before, take a moment to introduce this book, *Emotions & Essential Oils*, and discuss its basic premise: in addition to their physical properties, essential oils assist in emotional healing as well. Explain that you will be discussing both the physical and emotional properties of an essential oil at length.

2) Introduce the essential oil that you have chosen to highlight. You may want to discuss the reasons why you chose this specific essential oil to research and share for the class.

   Consider discussing the following information about the oil:
   - History, name (meaning of)
   - Plant type/species
   - Which part of the plant is used/distilled
   - The region of the world the plant is grown
   - Odor, intensity, what oils it blends well with
   - Chemical constituents
   - Common physical uses
   - Emotional properties of the oil

   As you discuss the physical properties of the oil, you may want to share scientific research or other studies you have gathered on that essential oil. As you explore the emotional properties of the oil, consider sharing personal experiences or other healing stories you have encountered in relation to that specific essential oil. Again, do not try to convince your audience that oils work on the emotional level. While offering a small amount of scientific background or evidence on the subject may be helpful to your audience, trying to convince or persuade individuals will never work. Be sensitive to the needs and maturity level of the specific group you are working with.

3) Consider creating interactive games or other activities to assist the learning of the group. You may want to use activities one or two from the audio lecture, *Emotions & Essential Oils: The Five Stages of Healing* (see Class Option A for more instructions on using this lecture in a class). Or create games and activities of your own.

4) You may want to offer practical suggestions on how to use the essential oil you have discussed. Also invite the class to apply the information by using the essential oil regularly and engaging with the oils through freewriting (see bonus track 10 from the audio lecture).

5) Wrap up the class. If you feel comfortable answering people's questions, take a few moments to do so.

Important Disclaimer:

These classes are for educational purposes only. None of the information contained in this section can or should be used as a means for prescribing or diagnosing another individual. There is no permission given or implied to practice counseling or therapy without a license. Those with psychological or emotional disorders should consult with a licensed healthcare professional for appropriate treatment. These classes should never be used as a substitute for professional counseling, support groups, or addiction recovery programs.